The Source for Processing Disorders

Gail J. Richard

Skills:	Auditory & Language Processing
Grades:	K and up
Ages:	5 and up

LinguiSystems, Inc.
3100 4th Avenue
East Moline, IL 61244-9700

1-800-PRO IDEA
1-800-776-4332

FAX: 1-800-577-4555
E-mail: service@linguisystems.com
Web: www.linguisystems.com

TDD: 1-800-933-8331
            (for those with hearing impairments)

Gail J. Richard, Ph.D., CCC-SLP, is a professor in the Department of Communication Disorders and Sciences at Eastern Illinois University in Charleston, IL. She teaches undergraduate and graduate courses and serves as a clinical supervisor for diagnostic and clinical practicum experiences. Gail enjoys the challenges presented in childhood developmental language disorders, such as autistic spectrum disorders, language processing disorders, language-learning disabilities, and selective mutism. Prior to her twenty years at Eastern, Gail's professional experience included working as a public school speech clinician and in a diagnostic/therapeutic preschool setting. She consults extensively with other professionals, teachers, parents, and school districts to assist in providing educational programming suggestions for children with special needs. Gail also presents numerous workshops, sharing her practical clinical knowledge with audiences around the country.

Gail's professional honors and awards include Fellow of the American Speech-Language-Hearing Association and the Illinois Speech-Language-Hearing Association, the Illinois Clinical Achievement Award, ASHA Legislative Council since 1991, Outstanding Alumnus Award at Southern Illinois University-Carbondale, five Faculty Excellence Awards at Eastern Illinois University, and the 2000 Distinguished Faculty Award and College of Science Scholar of the Year. Gail serves as the NCAA Faculty Athletics Representative at Eastern Illinois University, and she co-hosts a weekly TV sports program.

Gail's previous publications with LinguiSystems include *The Source for Autism; The Source for Treatment Methodologies in Autism; The Source for Syndromes* and *The Source for Syndromes 2,* co-authored with Debra Reichert Hoge; and *The Language Processing Test-Revised* and *Language Processing Kit,* co-authored with Mary Anne Hanner.

Dedication

To my parents for instilling confidence in me to pursue my dreams;

To my colleagues and students, who keep me excited about facing each new day;

To my clients and their parents, who continually challenge me to keep searching;

To Tache and Panther for welcoming me home each and every time after my travels and adventures!

Cover designed by Mike Paustian

Illustrations by Margaret Warner

Table of Contents

Preface

"The student has a processing disorder."

Have you heard that before? Probably more times than you care to mention. But do you really know what that means? Are you comfortable assessing and remediating the disorder? Do you feel like you know how to make a difference for the individual? And if you were asked, could you explain the difference between an auditory processing disorder and a language processing disorder?

If you answered *yes* to all of the questions, then pat yourself on the back and get on with your work. If you weren't quite sure how to respond and lack confidence in differentiating auditory processing, central auditory processing, language processing, etc., then this book is for you! And you are not alone in your dilemma. Many professionals struggle with the relationship between auditory and language processing disorders.

The purpose of *The Source for Processing Disorders* is to help professionals differentiate among processing disorders so that intervention efforts can become focused and more effective. Not all the answers are available yet, but research in the areas of audiology, speech-language pathology, psychology, neurology, and learning have certainly helped to sort out the critical aspects. *The Source for Processing Disorders* explains how to differentiate among the processing disorders, discusses the major processing models, explains assessment procedures, and outlines intervention strategies across types of processing disorders.

If you're ready for a great adventure and the answer to some of the challenges and confusion surrounding processing, then proceed forward. I hope you are able to process the information better than the gentleman in this cartoon—and that the outcome is more positive!

THE FAR SIDE   By GARY LARSON

THE FAR SIDE © 1988 FARWORKS, INC. All rights reserved.

"Wait a minute! ... McCallister, you fool!
This isn't what I said to bring!"

Chapter 1: Introduction to Processing Disorders

Background Information

In 1954, Myklebust introduced the term *auditory processing* to the field of audiology in *Auditory Disorders in Children.* Myklebust advocated careful diagnosis of auditory disorders to accurately differentiate types of problems children might be experiencing. Intervention needs varied dramatically, based on the type of processing disorder. Poor diagnosis and subsequent intervention could prevent children from developing their abilities to their full potential.

The term *processing* was introduced in conjunction with language about forty years ago by Vygotsky (1962) in a book called *Thought and Language.* Vygotsky was among the first to apply the term *process* to language by stating that the relation between thought and words is not a thing but a process, a continuous back-and-forth movement from thought to word and from word to thought.

Research and debate regarding "processing" intensified in the 1970s with Norma Rees' classic article entitled "Auditory processing factors in language disorders: The view from Procrustes' bed" (1973). The term was expanded to *central auditory processing* (Weisenberg & Katz, 1978) and defined as "the ability to receive and integrate auditory information." The actual unit of processing has been proposed to be as small as an individual phoneme to as large as major clauses in a sentence. Current debate continues to focus on the relationship and nature of processing as an auditory phenomenon, a language phenomenon, or both.

One aspect of processing disorders on which there is little disagreement is the impact the deficit has on learning. Johnson and Myklebust (1967) discussed a learning disabled student with a disturbance in processing that interfered with language comprehension and verbal expression. Cruickshank (1966) stated that most learning disabilities are the direct result of processing deficits. Gerber and Bryen (1981) stated that processing difficulties would result in school failure. Kirk and Bateman (1962) consistently applied the label *learning disabled* to children who had language problems that interfered with academic learning.

The significant detrimental impact of processing disorders on academic performance continues to be the focus of research today. Paula Tallal's extensive work on auditory perception concluded that children with language disorders have more difficulty with sound perception and sequences than normal children. Many language problems are the result of auditory perceptual impairments. Paula Tallal's work, paired with Dr. Michael Merzenich's, resulted in the creation of the Scientific Learning Corporation and *Fast ForWord* computer programs. Many of

Wiig and Semel's assessment tools and remediation programs grew from the observed learning difficulties experienced by children with language disorders.

Practicing speech-language pathologists and audiologists can provide numerous examples of processing deficits on their caseloads. The challenge is to sort out *auditory* versus *language* processing components so that intervention efforts meet each child's needs. As Myklebust emphasized in 1954, careful differential diagnosis is critical to effective intervention. If you work on the wrong problem, the disorder will not improve or resolve. Unfortunately, careful differential diagnosis continues to be a problem today!

A Processing Task

It is important to understand what *processing* is. While most professionals can cite behavioral and academic examples of processing, few can clearly explain what processing entails. It might be easier to begin with a concrete example of processing in a different sensory modality, the visual channel. Let's begin with a visual processing task. Imagine yourself back in a traditional student desk with the teacher showing this picture to the class and giving the instructions below the picture:

"All right, everyone. Look up here. Can you all see this? Okay, good. Now I want you to complete the following worksheet, answering the five questions about this item. You have fifteen minutes to finish, so get to work!"

Worksheet Questions

1. Where is the person in relation to the animal?
2. What direction is the animal facing?
3. Where in the United States might you see this?
4. What other things would you expect to see in the landscape?
5. Write a short story about the picture.

Now, if you are having difficulty answering the worksheet questions, it might be because you are not able to process the visual image. Your processing deficit is not part of visual acuity; you can see the black and white sections, but they are merely blobs to you. The problem is that you can't attach meaning to the black and white blobs. Staring at it longer or having the teacher show you personally doesn't help.

The teacher is likely to chastise you for not having your worksheet completed. It isn't that you don't understand the task or the questions; you can't make sense of the stimuli presented to you to then formulate a response. Your frustration might be building as all the other students complete their worksheets and turn them in. You might also begin to demonstrate some inappropriate behaviors as a result of your frustration. Welcome to the world of processing difficulty!

Several strategies could help you process the visual stimulus. Specific models will be discussed in subsequent chapters, but let me provide some top-down processing cues. You are using the **top-down model** when you process the big picture, or gestalt, of an idea and then fill in the details. Read these top-down cues one at a time, and keep track of when you finally "see" the image:

- The picture is of an animal and a person. (You might have guessed that from the worksheet questions.)

- The animal is a horse.

- The person is a cowboy.

- The horse is standing sideways in profile.

If the image suddenly popped out at you, then the cues provided the necessary orientation for you to process or attach meaning to the visual stimulus. If you still can't make sense of it, then we'll try some **bottom-up cues**. The bottom-up processing model provides details that help you build up to the gestalt or full image.

Bottom-up cues are harder to do on paper, but the picture is reproduced below with letters to accompany the bottom-up cues to help you process the visual image.

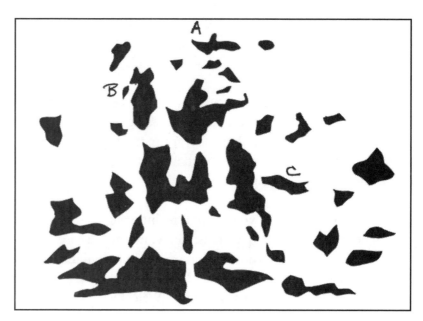

A = cowboy's hat

B = horse's head

C = horse's tail

The combination of cues has, hopefully, been successful in helping you "see" the visual image. If not, you are probably really frustrated by now, so the filled-in picture is provided on page 11.

This was a visual processing task, but it works well to illustrate some of the difficulties involved in auditory processing tasks. A few major points are highlighted in the following section.

The problem is not reception of the signal.

You could see the visual image; your eyes had received the visual image and taken the image into your brain for processing. The difficulty occurred after the sensory signal was received. The same is true for processing. We are not talking about children with auditory acuity problems; they can hear and receive auditory signals. With processing problems, an individual can't make sense of or attach meaning to a signal that has been received. Another example might be overhearing someone speaking in a foreign language that you don't know. You can hear the person talking, and, if you have a good ear for languages, you might even be able to repeat back what you heard, but you wouldn't be able to respond because you couldn't attach meaning to what you heard.

Repeating the signal is minimally helpful.

If the light is poor and you can't see the image well, that might compromise your ability to immediately process the visual image. However, staring at it intensely doesn't necessarily help and can escalate frustration. Teachers who repeat auditory stimuli louder or several times aren't necessarily helping the student with processing deficits. The redundancy might provide more processing time and refresh a signal that faded away or wasn't received accurately the first time, but processing deficits occur after receiving the signal. Abstracting meaning from the stimulus is the challenge in processing tasks.

Individuals process stimuli in different ways.

The top-down cues might have worked for some of you to finally "see" the picture. For others, those cues might not have helped at all and could have contributed to escalating your frustration or feeling of "dumbness." It might have been the bottom-up cues that provided the orientation for you to make sense of the image. When a teacher introduces information in only one manner, some students in the classroom probably don't benefit because they process information in a different manner. It is important to help teachers understand how to present information in a classroom so all students can benefit.

Cues provide orientation, not the answer.

We use context to assign meaning to stimuli. Without the cues, some of you would not have benefitted from my example. When teachers refuse to cue children or provide prompts, they prevent some students from using their skills to learn more. If the stimulus never becomes meaningful, learning doesn't occur. Teachers need to understand the importance of facilitating processing by providing context and a language-rich environment for presenting new information.

Processing occurs "on top of" basic knowledge.

The reason you couldn't complete the worksheet questions wasn't because you didn't know what the pictured animal or person was in the visual image. Processing is not a hearing acuity problem, such as deafness or being hard-of-hearing. It is also not a basic language-acquisition problem. The language knowledge has been acquired, but it can't be accessed because the signal isn't meaningful. Processing requires an individual to use basic auditory and language skills to complete more complex tasks with the information. This idea will be expanded upon significantly in later chapters.

A Definition of *Processing*

Massaro (1975) defined *processing* as "the ability to abstract meaning from an acoustic stimulus." In other words, processing is the ability to interpret or attach meaning to auditorily received information, to then formulate an expressive response. While this definition is rather broad, an auditory or language processing deficit can be more specifically defined. That is part of this book's objective: to provide operational definitions for the various processing deficits that allow professionals to differentiate among them in assessment and to provide treatment that makes a difference.

Pure processing problems are not attributable to other major disorders, such as mental retardation, emotional disabilities, motor-speech based disorders, neurological problems, auditory acuity problems, or language acquisition problems. People with processing disorders have normal intelligence, normal hearing acuity, and approximately age-commensurate performance on measurements of basic receptive and expressive vocabulary development. Processing deficits are subtle, but they eventually result in academic problems in reading, spelling, or other learning areas.

That is not to say that processing problems aren't evidenced in children with mental impairment, language disorders, or other disabilities, but the processing problems are imposed on top of the other auditory or language disorders associated with the primary disability. Differentiating processing disorders in the presence of other disabilities will also be addressed later in this book.

Bottom-up Versus Top-Down Processing Models

In the visual processing task example, I alluded to bottom-up versus top-down prompts to assist you in attaching meaning to the abstract picture. The bottom-up versus top-down models for attaching meaning to stimuli were among the first proposed within the profession and are still used today. The visual representation is presented below, with an explanation to follow.

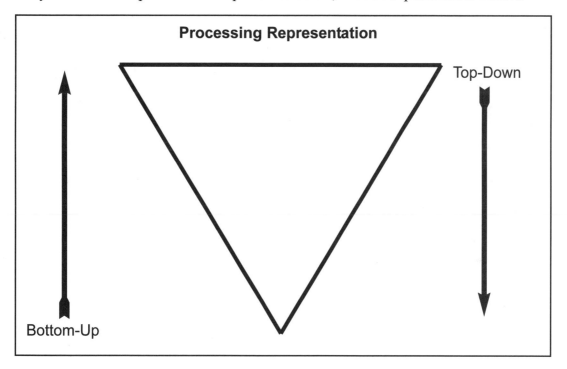

Bottom-Up Processing Model

The bottom-up processing model is often referred to as an "auditory processing model." This viewpoint was advocated by audiologists and served as their guideline for research, assessment, and intervention.

The bottom-up approach to processing begins with the acoustic signal. There has been extensive debate and research as to what the smallest unit of processing is, but most would agree that the phoneme is the beginning level of auditory processing. The individual hears a sound, which adds up to a series of phonemes, to a word, to a sentence, to the original message, which can be decoded for meaning. The acoustic aspects of the signal must be received before linguistic interpretation can occur.

Audiologists generally emphasize production and the acoustic output as critical to processing. The individual pieces of the signal must be processed gradually to build up to the whole. For example, a child is told to go retrieve something. To determine what to retrieve, he must attend to the acoustic features of the acoustic signal. The child hears /m/, then /æ/, and needs to wait for a /p/ or /t/ before he can linguistically process that he should go get his brother *Matt* or a *map*. Each acoustic piece of the signal is attended to, and they cumulatively add up to a word that is then processed for meaning as you move up the processing triangle.

Top-Down Processing Model

Speech-language pathologists generally use the top-down processing model to explain language processing. This model is referred to as a "gestalt" approach because the emphasis is on the "whole." Speech-language pathologists argue that we don't take the time to attend to every phoneme or acoustic piece of a signal. We quickly map on meaning, and then proceed down the processing triangle to pick out the necessary acoustic details for fine-tuning processing.

A top-down approach uses language knowledge and experiences within the world to interpret acoustic stimuli. A person hears an acoustic signal and uses general knowledge to glean meaning from a stimulus. The focus in this model is on the comprehension and intake of a signal. In the example above, the person begins by receiving the entire acoustic signal and quickly attaches meaning to the general content. He begins with the big picture—being asked to retrieve something. Once that aspect has been interpreted, he moves "down" to pay attention to details of the acoustic signal to determine if he should find a *map* or his brother *Matt*. A summary chart of the salient features is below.

Top-Down Processing Model	Bottom-Up Processing Model
Describes language processing	Describes auditory processing
Uses knowledge of language and the world to interpret acoustic signal	Attends to individual components of the acoustic signal before doing linguistic interpretation
Stresses comprehension and intake	Stresses production and output
Focus is on language/semantic knowledge	Focus is on acoustic knowledge
Speech-language pathologists' viewpoint	Audiologists' viewpoint

In reality, we all move back and forth on the model, sometimes processing with emphasis on general knowledge (top-down) and other times with emphasis on acoustic knowledge (bottom-up). A combination of both is also possible. A few examples will help illustrate application of the model.

- People tend to process new information using more of a bottom-up approach, while they process familiar information top-down. For example, when I teach the Introduction to Communication Disorders course, the undergraduate students are being exposed to new terminology for the first time. It is all very foreign to them, and they have minimal comfort with the material. I often see a sea of the tops of heads as they carefully write my every word. They rarely take the time to process what I am saying because it is novel; they want to get it recorded in their notes and hope to make sense of it later. I sometimes test the waters by reciting a ludicrous fact and see how long it takes before I see questioning eyes!

  On the other hand, when I teach graduate students, I see more eyes and can use facial expression as feedback to let me know if students are comprehending my content or if they are lost. They have heard the general information and are scaffolding new information onto knowledge with which they are comfortable. They tend to engage in top-down processing—they listen and then write notes that are not verbatim, but include the details they want to retain.

- Personal aptitude and subject matter also have an effect on the type of processing approach used. For example, I use computers as a tool to facilitate my work. I don't understand them; I simply know the commands to run certain software programs. If something goes wrong, I am in trouble. When I seek help, I write every-thing down as the computer specialist talks me through remedial steps. I function in a very bottom-up style when it relates to computers. My sister is a computer engineer who designs and deals with hardware. She speaks a different language when she talks about computers than I do. She is very top-down in her approach to computer conversations.

- The way we approach tasks also varies based on our personal preference for process-ing style. My brother is very bottom-up in his orientation. As children, when we had a new board game to play, he wanted to read the entire manual of rules before begin-ning. I wanted to read as the need arose and just start playing the game. To this day, I am the one who punches buttons until it works to program the VCR or run the microwave, only consulting the manual as a last resort.

- Sports is another example. For the non-sports enthusiast, attending a sporting event with a sports fan can be numbing. The bottom-up approach of asking a hundred questions to try to understand the event can be quite frustrating for the knowledgeable fan. The discrepancy between this mismatched pair can also create some tension! The fan who is extremely knowledgeable about the game might become testy or impatient and finally begin ignoring the struggling, bottom-up person's questions. It is so obvious to the knowledgeable person that he can't understand what is so hard for the novice.

This dilemma is what children often face in the school setting. A teacher, comfortable with the educational material, may teach in a top-down manner, yet many of the children in the classroom might need a bottom-up approach. The resulting discrepancy can lead to the teacher's misperceptions about some students' learning abilities. Educators must understand processing models and accommodate different styles among their students.

Reading programs are one concrete example of this problem. Phonics is a bottom-up approach to teaching reading. The alphabet letters are taught and paired with the acoustic sound that corresponds to that grapheme symbol. Words are taught by moving through the word letter-by-letter or sound-by-sound until you add up to the whole. Sight-word reading programs are more top-down in their approach. Word units are presented with functional meaning attached to them so that comprehension leads to word recognition.

Some children quickly lose patience and interest with phonic approaches to reading. Students who have central auditory processing problems are being taught through their weak link. Consequently, the processing problems bog down their reading progress. Reading is the core tool for other academic learning, so a negative domino effect begins in the academic realm. Children within the autistic spectrum need functional meaning attached to tasks to become interested in them. Phonic approaches to reading often sacrifice the meaning, and these children "check out" into their own world during reading activities.

Once again, teachers need to understand the ramifications of introducing reading through only one, very pure processing approach. Children need both skills—they need to be able to attach meaning to the word, but they also need to have phonics word-attack skills to determine what a new word is so they can attach appropriate meaning to it. It is important to supplement reading programs with activities incorporating processing from other perspectives to insure successful reading acquisition for more children in the classroom.

Processing is never as clear-cut as top-down or bottom-up; it isn't that simple or isolated. An understanding of the basic models, though, can make a huge difference in selecting and using an effective teaching presentation style.

The Neurology of Processing and Learning

Language shapes culture, language shapes thinking—and language shapes brains. The verbal bath in which a society soaks its children arranges their synapses and their intellects; it helps them learn to reason, reflect, and respond to the world.

Jane Healy, *Endangered Minds*

Learning changes the brain. Development of noninvasive medical technology has allowed scientists to better understand learning and its neurological connections. In the past, education and learning theories were based on behavioral observation. Now we have the technology to understand neurologically what is influencing the observed behavior.

Not only do we have that option, we have that responsibility. Education, particularly language aspects of learning, has been mired in behavior for decades. Teaching methodology and intervention techniques have been based in meaningless drill to "learn" new information. *How* children actually learned wasn't really important. Well, it's critically important now!

Research has shown that the brain rewires itself after each new experience. A stimulus to the brain starts the whole process. The stimulus is sorted and processed at several neurological levels on its pathway to being "learned." The brain literally grows new connections in response to environmental stimulation. Generating new connections based on neural stimulation is what "learning" is.

Myelination is another aspect of neurological maturation that is important in learning. Neural pathways become more efficient through myelination, a process of adding a fatty coating to axons. This coating increases efficiency in neural connections. Studies have shown that these new connections can happen within 48 hours of receiving a stimulus!

Neurology has also shown us that the brain modifies itself based on the type and amount of usage. The more meaningful the experience, the more intense the stimulation and the better the neurological activity, resulting in improved learning. "Getting smarter" means growing more synaptic connections and not losing existing connections.

The point is that processing is a neurological activity, not just a behavioral phenomena. Auditory processing and language processing cannot be discussed by just listing behaviors, goals, and activities. That type of therapy is over! Current efficacy is focused on accomplishing a functional difference in an individual's performance. Processing must be understood from a neurological perspective before behavioral differences can be achieved and intervention can be effective.

The Processing Continuum

Processing auditory stimuli occurs on a continuum, beginning with perception or reception of sound waves. The outer ear receives an acoustic signal and channels it into the middle ear and then the inner ear, where it is transferred to the auditory nerve. The auditory nerve moves the signal through the brainstem and to the upper cortex. Once it reaches the cortex, then language information can be attached to the signal.

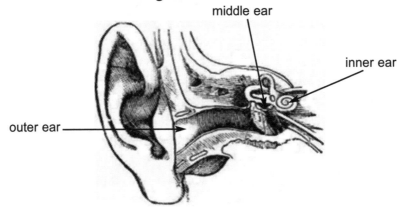

The anatomy and neurology of processing is covered in more depth in subsequent chapters of this book, but the important point to understand is that processing is just that, a process. Vygotsky was on the right track back in 1962 when he talked about moving back and forth between word and thought. More accurately, processing is moving back and forth between auditory features of the signal and language features of meaning. In other words, processing occurs on a continuum beginning at a level of pure auditory processing, transitions to a mix of both auditory and language processing, and ultimately ends in pure language processing. This processing continuum is diagrammed at the top of page 19.

Processing Terminology

When I first began exploring the area of processing disorders, the term commonly used in the literature was *auditory processing*. This term was used to refer to any auditory stimuli to which meaning was attached. At the time, it encompassed both of what has now been differentiated into central auditory processing and language processing disorders. If you read literature up to

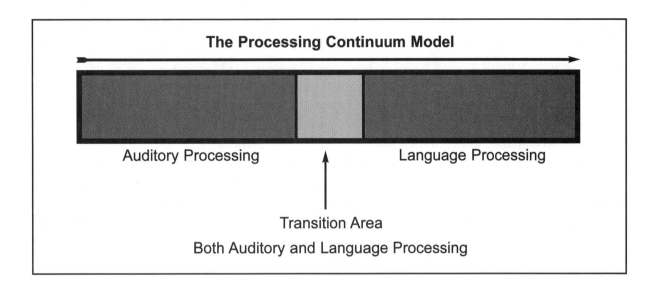

The Processing Continuum Model

Auditory Processing

Language Processing

Transition Area
Both Auditory and Language Processing

approximately the mid 1980s, the term *auditory processing* will include anything originating from an auditory stimulus. Many of the descriptions would now be categorized as *language processing.*

One of the most enlightening pieces of literature to highlight this confusion was a chapter written by Judy Duchan and Jack Katz in *Central Auditory Processing Disorders* (Lasky & Katz, 1983). The chapter began by describing the results of an audiological evaluation of a ten-year-old girl. Then a case evaluation conducted by a speech-language pathologist was presented. While there appeared to be no connection, the reader was later told that both cases summarize the same child assessed through different professional microscopes—audiology and speech-language pathology. Duchan and Katz very effectively illustrated that we tend to look at different aspects of behavior and function, depending on our professional orientation.

With further clinical and scientific research, *auditory processing* was gradually differentiated into *central auditory processing* and *language processing. Central auditory processing* referred to the central auditory nervous system (CANS), including the eighth auditory nerve through Heschl's gyrus in the cortex. *Language processing* referred primarily to cortical structures above the brainstem, beginning with Heschl's gyrus and focusing primarily on left temporal lobe language functions.

Consistency among terms has not been accomplished yet in the field of communication disorders. The term *auditory processing* still tends to encompass the entire continuum, while *central auditory processing* and *language processing* are used to differentiate between areas of neurological mediation. Sometimes *auditory processing* is used to describe the transition area when both auditory and language processing are being applied. My preference is to refer to the early part of the continuum, which deals with the CANS, as *central auditory processing (CAP)*. This processing entails accurately transferring a signal through the brainstem to the cortex. If the signal reaches the cortex unimpaired, then central auditory processing abilities are intact.

Language processing (LP) occurs post Heschl's gyrus, when an individual begins to use language knowledge to attach meaning to the signal. Layers of interpretation are hierarchically processed on the signal during language processing.

Other variables can interfere and contribute to what might appear to be central auditory or language processing disorders. Attention deficit disorder/attention deficit hyperactivity disorder (ADD/ADHD) results in faulty auditory processing, but the problem is likely to be in the reticular formation rather than the CANS or the temporal lobe. Oral-motor problems in the motor strip can prevent an accurate output response, yet the receptive processing might be intact. Word retrieval and memory problems are two additional variables that can significantly impact the ability to process auditory information accurately.

Processing Disorders

When a student has a disorder in processing auditory information, the consequences can be significant. Not only is academic learning at risk, but behavior problems often accompany the disorder. The frustration of having knowledge that you can't apply triggers a variety of emotional responses ranging from withdrawal and shutdown to aggressive, acting-out behaviors. The behavioral characteristics of central auditory processing and language processing deficits are addressed in Chapter 4 in this book.

Do you remember our cartoon friend Mr. McCallister's confusion of *off/on* from the Preface of this book on page 5? Suffice it to say, when meaning is not attached accurately to an auditory stimulus, the functional outcome can be dramatically different from expectations.

Chapter 2: Central Auditory Processing Model

The auditory system is much more complex than just two ears! Central auditory processing occurs after the ear has received the signal and begins to transfer the stimulus from the inner ear to the cortex via the central auditory nervous system (CANS). Central auditory processing focuses primarily on what occurs to the signal above the eighth auditory nerve as it moves through the brainstem and brain. It is important to have a working knowledge of the basic auditory neurology in order to accurately diagnose and remediate processing disorders.

Jeanane Ferre, an audiologist with specialization in central auditory processing disorders (CAPD), summarizes the extremely complex auditory system with a recitation listing "six different points to deal with information, four different pathways, four crossover points, one million cells to deal with auditory information, eight different cellular responses, and six different cell types." The CANS is an exquisite system!

I acknowledge the following to be a very cursory view of the auditory systems. It is not my intention to explore auditory neurology in great detail; I am not qualified to do so. There are excellent textbooks and professionals that can expound in great detail on the intricacies of the system. My intention is to highlight the major structures and functions to provide a rudimentary working knowledge of the system for clinical application.

While you might be tempted to skip the next sections and move on to the practical clinical information—don't! I will attempt to make the information "user friendly," but one of the mistakes we have sometimes made in audiology and speech-language pathology is to attempt assessment and intervention without a model. The result is "hit and miss" therapy with minimal effectiveness. We are not in control if we don't understand the premise behind a particular diagnosis or intervention program. Taking time to understand the neurological models will increase your confidence and autonomy in delivering services.

Anatomy and Physiology of the Auditory System

The anatomy of the ear is what many non-audiologists consider to be the auditory anatomy of importance. While it is important, it is merely the surface level of auditory processing, referred to as the *peripheral auditory system*. Audiometric tests to evaluate hearing acuity in the outer, middle, and inner ear are prerequisite to central auditory processing (CAP) assessment. An individual must be able to perceive acoustic stimuli adequately in both ears to undergo CAP testing.

The diagram below summarizes the transference of the acoustic signal through the ear to the central auditory nervous system (CANS).

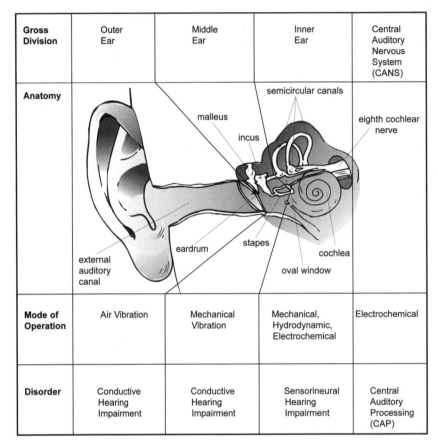

Gross Division	Outer Ear	Middle Ear	Inner Ear	Central Auditory Nervous System (CANS)
Anatomy				
Mode of Operation	Air Vibration	Mechanical Vibration	Mechanical, Hydrodynamic, Electrochemical	Electrochemical
Disorder	Conductive Hearing Impairment	Conductive Hearing Impairment	Sensorineural Hearing Impairment	Central Auditory Processing (CAP)

Transference of the Acoustic Signal Through the Ear

The acoustic signal is received by the outer ear. The sound is carried as vibration in air and moves through the external auditory canal to the eardrum. The vibration of the eardrum changes the stimulus to a mechanical vibration as it enters the middle ear and is passed along through the ossicular chain, which is comprised of the malleus (hammer), the incus (anvil), and the stapes (stirrup). At the oval window, the mechanical energy stimulates fluid in the semicircular canals to change the stimulus into hydrodynamic energy as it enters the inner ear and moves through the cochlea. The stimulus is changed once again, this time into electrochemical energy as it moves into the eighth cochlear nerve for transference through the brainstem to the upper cortex of the brain.

Damage in the outer or middle ear results in conductive hearing impairments, in that the acoustic stimulus cannot be conducted effectively through the ear structures. Many conductive losses are temporary and can be corrected if diagnosed early, such as otitis media (infection in the middle ear). Hearing aids can often compensate effectively for conductive hearing losses. Deficits in the inner ear structures result in sensorineural hearing impairments, which are permanent and have a greater impact on a person's ability to function. Cochlear implants are an option for some individuals, but many sensorineural losses must be compensated for through sign language and other non-auditory means of input for stimuli.

Impairments in the peripheral auditory system are classified as a *hearing impairment* and are designated as *mild, moderate,* or *severe* based on the degree of loss. The primary focus of intervention is using alternative methods to enhance the acoustic signal or to compensate for compromised input.

The central auditory nervous system (CANS) is diagramed below. The stimulus is electrochemical energy as it moves through the brainstem and brain structures. The CANS structures are evaluated during a central auditory processing (CAP) assessment. Each level is labeled for you to follow transference of the acoustic signal as it moves through the central auditory nervous system.

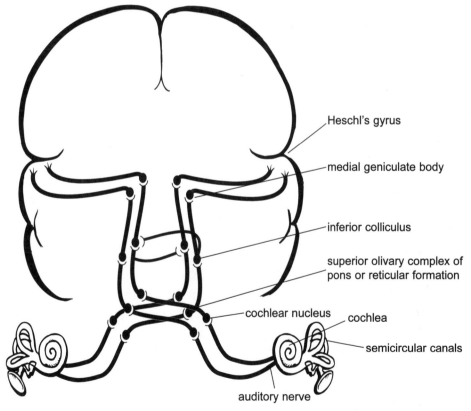

Heschl's gyrus

medial geniculate body

inferior colliculus

superior olivary complex of pons or reticular formation

cochlear nucleus   cochlea

semicircular canals

auditory nerve

The Central Auditory Nervous System

The central auditory pathways originate in the spiral ganglion and terminate in the temporal lobe of the cortex at Heschl's gyrus. Multiple afferent (ascending) and efferent (descending) pathways provide neural redundancy. Several crossover points in the neural pathways also add to neural redundancy.

The fibers of the spiral ganglion are stimulated by the organ of Corti. These fibers extend to form the cochlear nerve and terminate at the cochlear nuclei after entering the brainstem. At this point, acoustic messages have been transferred to the ipsilateral (same side) cochlear nuclei.

The neurons then proceed to the superior olivary complex of the pons or the reticular formation. At this level, the CANS begins to have bilateral representation of the acoustic signal. The binaural phenomena of crossover originates at this level of the brainstem. At this point, there is already ipsilateral and contralateral routing of neurological fibers. It is also important to note that the contralateral (opposite side) pathways are dominant over the ipsilateral (same side) pathways. This concept will be revisited later in this chapter. The reticular formation is also an important structure that will be revisited in the next chapter in discussion of the anatomy for language processing. The reticular formation is responsible for screening all the sensory input entering the brainstem level and determining which stimuli is sent on to the upper cortex for processing. The reticular formation also functions as the arousal mechanism for the upper cortex to alert it to incoming stimuli.

From the superior olivary complex on each side of pons, fibers extend to the inferior colliculi at the level of the midbrain. There is additional crossover, or bilateral representation, at this level. Some rudimentary processing also occurs at this level.

The auditory neural fibers then proceed to the medial geniculate bodies. This is the final subcortical level in the CANS prior to entering the cortex. By this point, crossover has occurred. From here, the auditory pathways spread to the cortex, specifically Heschel's gyrus in the temporal lobe of the brain.

The crossover of neural fibers in the ascending auditory tract insures that acoustic impulses originating in one cochlea eventually reach both auditory cortices. This bilateral representation for each ear accounts for the signal redundancy in the auditory neural pathways. Consequently, auditory information is represented bilaterally and can be processed on both sides. This bilateral redundancy is fundamental to the principles of central auditory processing assessment.

Additional redundancy is supplied by the corpus collosum, which provides communication between the left and right hemispheres of the brain. The left hemisphere is usually dominant for language, so the interhemispheric communication is essential to match acoustic input with language knowledge.

Neurological Maturation of the Auditory System

The auditory system is a complex, redundant neurological structure. Research suggests that myelinization of the CANS system can take up to seven years in children. The anatomy and physiology of the upper cortex for language will be addressed in Chapter 3. However, the continuum of processing that was explained in Chapter 1 begins in development of the auditory system.

Development of language appears to parallel neuromaturational development of the auditory system. Research has consistently suggested that children with language disorders have trouble making auditory perceptual judgments. Language development seems to occur with increased neural connections. Several aspects of neurological maturation contribute to these assumptions.

- Specific neural connections are prerequisite for both cognitive and language growth. As dendritic connections between neural structures increase, more synaptic connections are formed; the ability to process information begins to develop and increase.

- Adequate reception of acoustic signals is needed to analyze language components. Maturation of the CANS precedes upper cortex maturation, meaning that signals must reach the brain to stimulate the neural connections for language processing.

- Brain maturation proceeds from inner to outer, or deep brain out to the cortex. It also means that deep cortex precedes outer cortex functions. Maturation dictates that inner brain structures must develop to get to the outer brain structures.

- Eighty percent of the cortex is association areas. The association fibers myelinate late and are more susceptible to maturation problems. For example, the association fibers between Broca's area and the angular gyrus are not completely myelinated until ages nine to eleven.

These aspects of neurological maturation begin to suggest the reason for more language processing disorders than central auditory processing disorders. The central auditory system has incredible redundancy and develops early. The cortex structures develop later and rely on the corpus collosum for interhemispheric communication, which may take up to eleven years to reach full neurological development.

There are also many neurological asymmetries in maturation due to the manner in which our species develops. Language is usually lateralized in the left hemisphere, resulting in several right and left dichotomies in neural maturation, as listed on page 26.

- Linguistic information is processed in the left hemisphere; non-linguistic information is processed in the right hemisphere.

- Analytical information is processed in the left hemisphere; gestalt information is processed in the right hemisphere.

- Sequential capabilities, logic, sentence structure, etc., are processed in the left hemisphere; visual, spatial, and holistic information are processed in the right hemisphere.

Anatomic evidence supports the fact that the left hemisphere structure is larger in most people. This finding occurs throughout the primary structures involved in auditory and language processing.

- Heschl's gyrus is seven times larger in the left than the right hemisphere.

- Broca's area is longer in the left hemisphere than the right.

- The post-temporal area is larger in the left hemisphere than the right.

Philosophy of Central Auditory Processing

The central auditory nervous system (CANS) is responsible for transferring an auditory signal through the brainstem and into the cortex, where it will be processed within a language code modality. If a signal reaches the brain intactly, then central auditory processing ability is basically normal. A central auditory processing disorder involves an auditory stimulus that becomes distorted or compromised in some way before the brain has received it to act upon. If certain acoustic features of the signal cannot be perceived accurately (auditory discrimination), then the breakdown is probably in the overlap transition area of Heschl's gyrus in the cortex.

The premise of central auditory processing (CAP) assessment is that the brain looks for consistency in processing an auditory signal. If the brain receives a confusing signal, an abnormal behavioral response will result. The assumption for conducting CAP testing is that something in the central auditory nervous system (CANS) isn't working properly. The purpose of CAP assessment is to evaluate the brainstem and cortical function of the CANS by stressing the auditory system or making the task harder. This task is accomplished by eliminating or reducing redundancy in the signal, which compromises what the CANS receives.

An understanding of the redundancy and contralateral dominance in the process is important to adequately comprehend central auditory processing. The CANS has external redundancy in that acoustic stimuli is usually represented bilaterally. That is, both ears hear something at the same time. The internal redundancy is provided by the crossover points to represent the acoustic message bilaterally several times during the neurological transfer to the cortex.

To illustrate these concepts, we are going to conduct a race within the central auditory nervous system. A simplified diagram of the CANS is provided to assist. First, here is a reiteration of the internal redundancy in the CANS system.

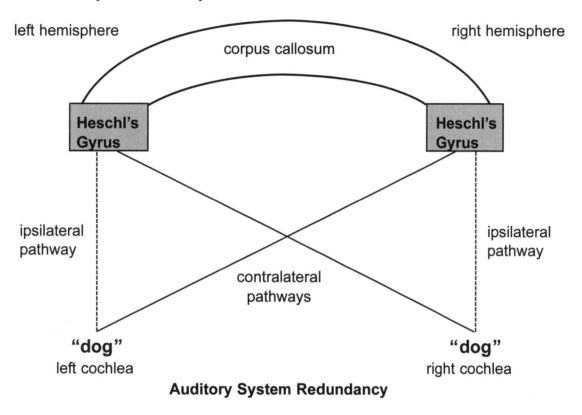

Auditory System Redundancy

Each ear will receive the same word at the same time. Both the right and left cochleas hear the word *dog*.

From the right ear/cochlea, *dog* travels up the ipsilateral pathways to Heschl's gyrus in the right hemisphere. Then the signal crosses over to the left hemisphere via the corpus collosum. At the same time from the right ear/cochlea, the word *dog* travels up the contralateral pathway to Heschl's gyrus in the left hemisphere, and then it crosses over to the right hemisphere Heschl's gyrus via the corpus collosum.

At the same time, the word *dog* was received by the left ear/cochlea. It also has contralateral and ipsilateral pathways to Heschl's gyri in the left and right hemispheres, as well as use of the corpus collosum for interhemispheric communication to check and match the signal.

What should become very apparent is the incredible internal redundancy built into the central auditory nervous system. A signal has to be significantly compromised not to reach the target destination. The sequence of crossovers and checks on bilateral hemispheric receipt of the signal is amazing!

Now let's run a race which stresses the system to check integrity of the CANS. The rules of the race are the following:

- The first word to reach the left temporal lobe Heschl's gyrus wins.

- Contralateral pathways are more efficient than ipsilateral pathways.

- The ears will receive different signals this time and "race" to the left temporal lobe.

This time, the left ear will hear the word *hot;* the right ear will hear *dog.* This procedure is called *dichotic signal presentation,* (*di* meaning "two" and *chotic* meaning "different"); two ears receive different signals at the same time.

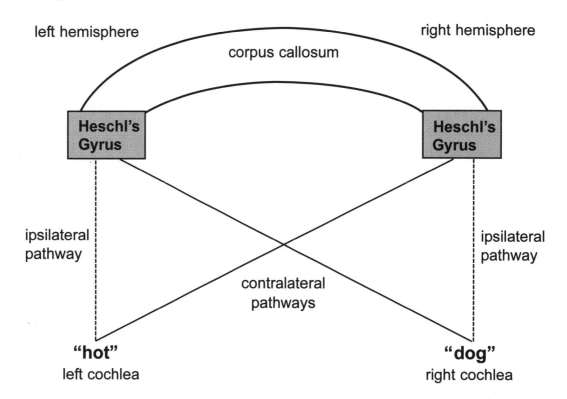

So the race begins. Both ears have ipsilateral and contralateral pathways as well as a corpus collosum for interhemispheric transference. Which word will reach the left temporal lobe Heschl's gyrus first? Or in which order will the left hemisphere hear the words for processing: *dog - hot* or *hot - dog*?

If you said *dog - hot,* you deserve a gold star! Remember that as a species, we are wired stronger for contralateral dominance, so the word heard in the right ear/cochlea will reach the left Heschl's gyrus via the dominant contralateral pathways quicker, beating out the ipsilateral pathway of *hot* from the left ear and the contralateral pathway to right hemisphere and then back to left via the corpus collosum. That is what is meant by *right-sided dominance;* sensory input received by the right ear, eye, hand, foot, etc., is dominant, but it is mediated in the left hemisphere of the brain.

Because of the built-in redundancy of the auditory pathways, the normal listener can tolerate a degree of variability in an auditory signal. Attaching meaning to acoustic input isn't dependent on receiving every formant of the signal. A normal listener uses a constructive process when listening to an acoustic stimulus and can fill in distorted segments using language knowledge. In other words, acoustic information is combined with linguistic information to attach meaning to the auditory signal.

For this reason, an individual with a defective auditory neurological system might respond appropriately. CAP testing must degrade the auditory signal so that the normal redundancies are absent. The CANS must be challenged to interpret the acoustic signal. How this is accomplished will be explained further in Chapter 5: Processing Assessment. The important point to remember is that CAP tests should minimize the influence of language, cognition, and other upper-cortex skills while maximizing the function of the CANS.

Okay, that wasn't too bad, was it? The outline of the progression for CANS on page 30 summarizes the central auditory processing model. The next chapter continues building upon these principles. In the meantime, stay tuned for new research discoveries.

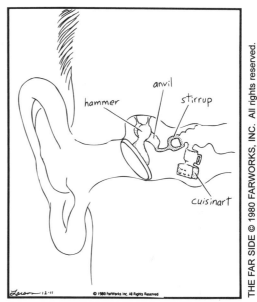

THE FAR SIDE   By GARY LARSON

Professor Harold Rosenbloom's diagram of the middle ear, proposing his newly discovered fourth bone.

Central Auditory Nervous System (CANS) Outline

A. Complex auditory system
1. Auditory pathways originate in spiral ganglion and terminate in cortex of temporal lobe
2. Multiple afferent and efferent pathways provide neurological redundancy
3. Several crossover points in neural pathways

B. Spiral ganglion fibers stimulated by organ of Corti
1. Fibers extend to form cochlear nerve
2. Terminate at cochlear nuclei after entering brainstem
3. Message transferred to ipsilateral cochlear nuclei

C. Neurons proceed to reticular formation (superior olivary complex of pons or SOC)
1. Start bilateral representation; crossover terminating in SOC
2. Ipsilateral and contralateral routing fibers
3. Binaural phenomenon originates at this level of the brainstem
4. Contralateral dominant over ipsilateral in neural transmission

D. Reticular formation
1. Clearinghouse for sensory stimuli
2. Integrates information with neural network
3. Arouses cortex to interpret incoming stimuli

E. From SOC, fibers extend to inferior colliculi at midbrain
1. Additional crossover
2. Some rudimentary processing

F. Fibers then extend to medial geniculate bodies
1. Crossover has occurred by this point
2. Final subcortical level in CANS prior to cortex
3. Auditory radiations spread to Heschl's gyrus in cortex

G. Heschl's gyrus
1. Brodman areas 41 and 42
2. First level of auditory reception in cortex
3. Bilateral cortical representation; signal redundancy in neural pathways
4. Crossovers insure impulses originating from one cochlea reach both auditory cortices

H. Corpus collosum
1. Communication between hemispheres
2. Added redundancy

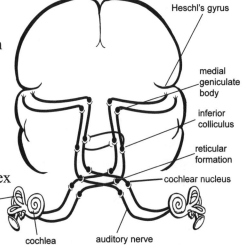

Heschl's gyrus

medial geniculate body

inferior colliculus

reticular formation

cochlear nucleus

semicircular canals

cochlea

auditory nerve

Chapter 2: Quick Quiz Questions

Match the following functions with the anatomical structure involved in the Central Auditory Nervous System (CANS).

A. Auditory nerve

B. Superior olivary complex

C. Heschl's gyrus

D. Corpus collosum

E. Cochlear nucleus

F. Inferior colliculus

G. Medial geniculate bodies

1. ____ First level of bilateral representation of the auditory signal

2. ____ Second level of binaural representation, or crossover

3. ____ Originates from fibers extending from the spiral ganglion

4. ____ Provides communication between hemispheres

5. ____ Auditory nerve enters the brainstem at this structure

6. ____ Last subcortical level in the CANS

7. ____ First cortical level in the CANS

Fill in the blanks from the following word bank. Not all of the words are used, and words can only be used once.

contralateral	signals	right	redundancy
ipsilateral	temporal	left	stress

8. _____ auditory pathways are more efficient than _____ pathways.

9. Language is lateralized to the _____ _____ lobe.

10. The premise of central auditory processing (CAP) assessment is to _____ the

auditory system by reducing _____.

(Answers are on page 184.)

Chapter 3: Language Processing Model

In Chapter 1, a sketch of the processing continuum was introduced (see page 19). Based on information presented in Chapter 2 outlining the Central Auditory Processing Model, the continuum can be further refined to better represent the material covered so far.

The Processing Continuum Model

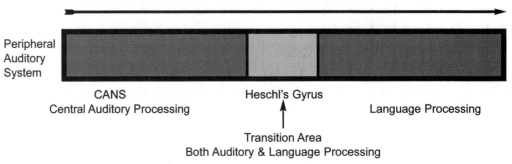

Hearing acuity, or adequate peripheral hearing ability, is prerequisite to processing auditory stimuli. The processing continuum begins where the peripheral auditory system stops and the central auditory nervous system (CANS) begins (the eighth auditory nerve). Central auditory processing follows the neurological pathway of the auditory signal to where it enters the cortex at Heschl's gyrus, the first cortical area that processes speech and language information from the auditory signal.

Auditory information comes into the system and is processed within 400 milliseconds. Some rudimentary processing has been completed at the brainstem level to determine if the auditory stimulus is important and should proceed to the cortex for decoding. At Heschl's gyrus, auditory features of the signal are determined using language knowledge. Very functionally-defined types of auditory processing skills occur at this overlap site, such as auditory discrimination, auditory figure-ground, auditory closure, etc. These will be defined later.

This is the point at which the processing model picks up in this chapter. Once speech we hear enters the temporal lobe, particularly the left temporal lobe through Heschl's gyrus, we begin to switch from an auditory processing mode to a language processing mode.

Once again, bear with the neurology review. The pieces of the puzzle have to be generated before they can all fit together and form an identifiable picture. The black and white splotches from Chapter 1 will all fit together by the end of this chapter!

Anatomy and Physiology of the Language System

Neuropsychology is the science of understanding how behaviors are related to brain function. All behavior is mediated by the central nervous system, which includes the brain, the brainstem, and the spinal cord. Any impairment in the central nervous system will interfere with learning. Research has demonstrated that specific functions are localized in the brain, yet the whole brain is involved in processing.

Research has well supported the premise that brain structures all play highly specific roles in behavior and are all under coordinated control. Every mental activity is affected through joint activity of discrete cortical units. When one system fails, behavior is adversely affected. However, through remediation and compensation, other parts of the brain can secondarily resume that function, and the behavior returns in a limited way. Effective diagnosis needs to examine behavior to determine which system has experienced failure. Then intervention can focus more specifically on the discrete function some other system in the brain must assume secondarily. While that information sounds complex, it's really rather simple and makes a lot of sense in clinical application.

A. R. Luria (1970) proposed a model called the *Functional Organization of the Brain*. Although the model is somewhat dated, it provides an excellent model for diagnosis of and intervention for developmental deficits. Gaddes (1980) applied Luria's model very effectively to language and learning by integrating neurological development and maturation with observed behavioral responses to guide remedial intervention. The model reinforces the central auditory nervous system orientation and expands to explain cortical organization for language processing.

Functional Organization of the Brain divides the central nervous system into three functional units.

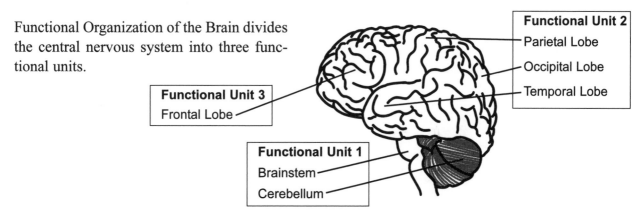

Functional Unit 3
Frontal Lobe

Functional Unit 1
Brainstem
Cerebellum

Functional Unit 2
Parietal Lobe
Occipital Lobe
Temporal Lobe

The first functional unit is the reticular formation. This brainstem structure (the midbrain, pons, and medulla oblongata) was included in the CANS. The reticular formation is responsible for the neurological readiness of the central nervous system to interact with the environment. It also serves as the energy supply system for the cortex by maintaining an attentive state to incoming stimuli. The *reticular activating system,* as it is sometimes called, awakens the brain and keeps it alert. It also directs neural traffic by determining which stimuli proceed on up to the cortex. In attention deficit disorder, this is the general problem area. The reticular formation doesn't effectively sort through the incoming stimuli and sends all the input on to the cortex, resulting in confused behavior as an individual has to consciously determine which stimuli to focus on. The reticular system is a critical unit for processing.

The second functional unit consists of the parietal, occipital, and temporal lobes. The second functional unit is responsible for isolating neural impulses into discrete areas for analysis, storage, coding, and organization. Visual stimuli is processed in the occipital lobes, tactile stimuli is processed in the parietal lobes, and auditory stimuli is processed in the temporal lobes. Each cortical section is further delineated into three zones. We'll come back and explore the second functional unit in more detail in a moment.

The third functional unit is the frontal lobes. This unit is responsible for active responses through motoric expression to stimuli that have been processed in the second functional unit. In addition, planning and managing a person's behavior in relation to perceptions and knowledge is mediated in the third functional unit.

The second functional unit is where processing occurs in the cortex. Each lobe of the second functional unit has a primary, secondary, and tertiary zone with discrete functions.

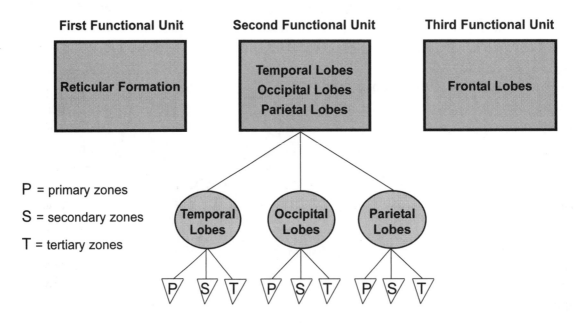

The primary zone (P) is responsible for receiving the incoming neural impulse. Visual information enters the cortex in the primary zone of the occipital lobe, tactile information enters the cortex in the primary zone of the parietal lobe, and auditory information enters the cortex in the primary zone of the temporal lobe. The primary zone is not involved in detailed processing, only in the sensation of the signal as meaningful in that sensory modality and in the discrimination of its primary features. An impairment in the primary zone would be a sensory impairment, not a higher-order processing impairment.

The secondary zone (S) is responsible for processing incoming information and attaching meaning to sensory input received in the primary zone. Visual meaning or processing occurs in the secondary zone of the occipital lobe, tactile processing occurs in the secondary zone of the parietal lobe, and attaching meaning to auditory stimuli occurs in the secondary zone of the temporal lobe. Interpretation is completed by decoding, organizing, associating with previous information, and storing into memory for future use. The secondary zones are the association zones of the cortex where stimuli are integrated into meaningful experiences.

The tertiary zone (T) is designed for multisensory neural integration. Higher-level processing is completed in the tertiary zone, building on the processing that has already occurred in secondary zones. The tertiary zone integrates new information with old (stored) information and integrates discrete neural impulses among sensory modalities. In other words, the tertiary zone is where information from all cortices is integrated (tactile, visual, and auditory). It is also where the neurological system transfers from a passive, receptive processing of input into an active, expressive output.

At this point, it would be helpful to visualize the second functional unit and assign some neurological landmark structures to tie some of this information together. The diagrams on page 36 will also allow us to further explore the temporal lobe, the second functional unit, where language processing primarily occurs.

Diagram A illustrates the primary zones for each of the lobes in the second functional unit. This is where sensory stimuli enter the cortex from the brainstem. In the left temporal lobe, the primary zone is Brodmann areas 41 and 42, which is Heschl's gyrus. The CANS left off when the auditory stimuli entered the cortex at Heschl's gyrus. That is exactly where the functional units theory picks up, at the primary sensation area in the brain—Heschl's gyrus. Therefore, Heschl's gyrus is that overlap area where an auditory stimulus is being partially processed for its acoustic features (auditory processing) and meaning is being attached based on symbolic knowledge (language processing).

Diagram A: Primary Zones

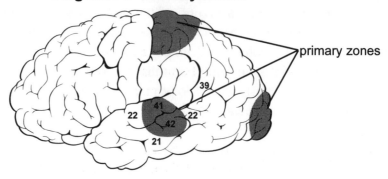

primary zones

Diagram B: Secondary Zones

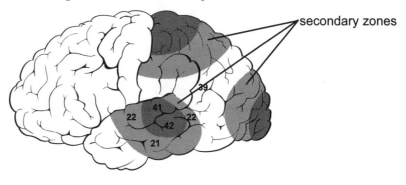

secondary zones

Diagram C: Tertiary Zone

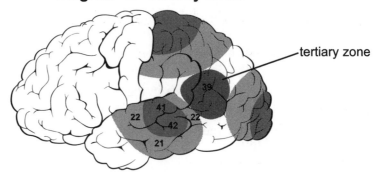

tertiary zone

In the previous chapter, it was explained that 80% of the cortex is association areas. These areas correspond to the secondary zones, or associative processing areas, for each of the lobes in the second functional unit. If you look at Diagram B, you will notice that the secondary zones wrap around the primary zones. The sensory stimuli enter the cortex and fan out into the processing areas to code, organize, interpret, and attach layers of meaning to the stimuli received. In the left temporal lobe, where language is located, the association areas are Brodmann numbers 21 and 22. A familiar landmark in this area is Wernicke's area, which corresponds to Brodmann 22.

Once processing within the discrete modality has occurred, higher-level processing can occur by integrating across sensory modalities. This integration is accomplished in the tertiary zone, shown in Diagram C. While each lobe has a tertiary zone, it is a common area where all the secondary zones intersect. The anatomical structure is the angular gyrus, Brodmann area 39, which mediates integration of sensory input. Probably one of the most obvious examples of a tertiary zone skill is reading. The visual graphemes (occipital) must be integrated with experiences (parietal) and language knowledge (temporal) for a person to comprehend the printed word effectively. In fact, studies on dyslexia support problems in the area of the angular gyrus. When blood flow during reading is examined in normal readers, the blood flow is concentrated in area 39. For children with dyslexia, the blood flow is diffused and not focused in this area.

The other major function of the angular gyrus is to integrate into the next functional unit for motoric output. Transference from receptive processing to an expressive response requires activation of Brodmann 44, or Broca's area, and the motor strip in the frontal lobe. The corpus collosum, also imposed on the language processing model, provides the interhemispheric communication to seek a match in sensory stimuli and processing efforts. The chart below summarizes the language processing model at the level of the left temporal lobe.

Language Processing Model—Left Temporal Lobe

	Primary Zone	Secondary Zone	Tertiary Zone
Function	Auditory Sensation	Attach Meaning	Integrate Auditory Information
Purpose	Auditory Integration	Language Integration	Cortical Integration
Brodmann #	41, 42	21, 22	39
Anatomical Structure	Heschl's Gyrus	Wernicke's +	Angular Gyrus
Summary	**Auditory Input**	**Processing**	**Integration to Output**

Neurological Maturation of the Language Processing System

A quick review of major anatomical maturation notes from Chapter 2, pages 25-26, might be enlightening; the second time around, the information might make more sense because a few more neurological pieces have now been filled in. The following section highlights previous information and builds upon that knowledge.

First, several anatomical structures are larger in the left hemisphere. The importance of those structures in language processing should be clearer now. These structures include the following:

- **Heschl's gyrus**, the primary reception area for inputting auditory stimuli to cortex for language processing

- The **angular gyrus**, the tertiary zone in the post temporal lobe area, responsible for cortical integration across sensory modalities

- **Broca's area**, in the third functional unit motor strip, responsible for motoric output

The language processing model further supports a hierarchical integration of processing following a neuromaturational order of the zones. The previous chapter discussed how the cortex matures from inner (deep) to outer (surface). Neuromaturation in the language processing model corresponds and continues where the CANS model stopped. Research supports that the zones of the second functional unit develop maturationally in order: primary, secondary, tertiary. Heschl's gyrus is the primary zone for processing and the first to develop. The association areas (secondary zone) fan out from the primary zone and myelinate later. The tertiary zone is the last to mature and the most susceptible to problems. The connections between the angular gyrus and Broca's area are the last to myelinate completely, which explains the difficulty children with processing problems have in coordinating an expressive response quickly and accurately. The integrity of the neural connections between receptive processing and expressive output may be questionable in these children.

The processing models correspond with neuromaturational development, but they also help to explain the behavioral hierarchy of processing.

- The continuum of processing entails a progressive attachment of meaning to an auditory stimulus.

- It supports the contribution of each level in the hierarchy.

- It integrates the entire nervous system in the processing task.

A final step is to revisit the processing continuum and add the language processing model components. The Processing Continuum Model now reflects the full continuum of processing, with central auditory processing and language processing defined in terms of neurological structures and sites responsible for dealing with the sensory stimuli.

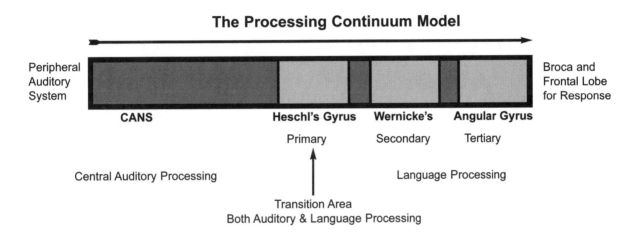

The next chapters will explain the observed characteristics and behaviors that are mediated by the defined neurology, followed by assessment and remediation using the neurological models.

Philosophy of Language Processing

Language processing is the ability to attach meaning to an auditory signal using parameters of the linguistic system, such as semantic knowledge. The premise is that foundations of language are developed, but competency using those foundations to climb a hierarchical ladder of complexity is impaired.

The language processing model supports the concept of hierarchical attachment of meaning. The auditory signal travels through the CANS into the cortex, with a progressive attachment of meaning to the stimulus as it moves through the primary, secondary, and tertiary zones. Each level contributes to an increased linguistic complexity of attaching meaning to the stimulus. The model identifies discrete skill areas, but it also integrates the entire nervous system into the processing task. While this explanation is somewhat simplistic and neurological dividers are never as absolute as defined in this chapter, the model provides an idea of how to sample central nervous system activity through carefully designed tasks.

The neuropsychological Processing Continuum Model defines behavior as a function of central nervous system (CNS) activity. Assuming that the CNS functions systematically, behaviors can be observed that substantiate intact neurology for processing. The assumption also applies to deficits. Assuming that the system dysfunctions systematically, it should be possible to measure children's skills that reflect systematic CNS patterns. Deficits should be demonstrated on more than one task if the behavior is a reflection of CNS function.

That's one of the greatest strengths of the Processing Continuum Model—it serves remediation efforts in an objective neurological manner. Audiology has already been grounded in an objective neurological model. Audiologists' assessment instruments evaluate the integrity of auditory neurological structures. Their intervention is designed based on the neurological functioning capabilities of the system.

On the other hand, speech-language pathologists have been guessing at language processing abilities for decades by using results from various evaluation subtests. When a test is given and a child performs poorly on a subtest, a goal is written to drill that deficit skill. The clinician has no idea why the child did poorly on that task or if the child has the prerequisite language skills to learn that task; because it was in error, it is drilled. The Processing Continuum Model allows speech-language pathologists to move away from the "hit and miss" game and embrace a model based on neurological integrity.

The other major contribution of the Processing Continuum Model is an explanation of how and where deficits occur. Let's explore the second functional unit in terms of using it as a deficit model.

Functional Unit 2

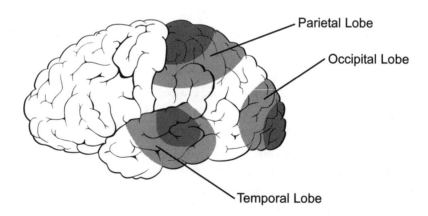

Parietal Lobe

Occipital Lobe

Temporal Lobe

If a child is diagnosed as blind, then we know the occipital primary zone is not going to function. Visual sensory stimuli won't be able to enter the cortex through the primary zone due to the visual acuity problem. The same is true for a child who is diagnosed as deaf. The primary zone of the temporal lobe won't function to bring auditory stimuli into the cortex.

As professionals, we are very good at understanding primary zone deficits and compensating for them. No one tells the blind child to keep looking at something until he sees it! A deaf child is not accused of "not trying" and made to listen to tapes until he hears the sound! Professionals easily acknowledge primary zone deficits and compensate to get information into the cortex for processing through other means. A blind child uses braille or touch (tactile/primary zone parietal lobe) or sound (primary zone temporal lobe) to get sensory stimuli into the cortex so it can be channeled to the association secondary zones for processing. A deaf child still learns to process language; the language is simply introduced to the cortex in a different primary zone and uses the tertiary zone as the gate back into the secondary zone temporal lobe for language processing.

The problem arises when the deficit is in the secondary or tertiary zones of the second functional unit. The association areas of the cortex account for approximately 80% of the brain, a large amount of space as compared to the primary zones. It is quite likely that secondary zone deficits occur with greater frequency than primary zone deficits due to larger cortex area that can be damaged or compromised later in neurological maturation, yet professionals have a hard time acknowledging secondary and tertiary zone deficits as legitimate. The children are blamed for not trying hard enough, not paying attention, or not applying themselves. Weak tasks are not compensated for; instead, children are drilled in their deficits. This approach is very incongruent with what we know about neurology and primary zone deficits. Intervention has to use other modalities to compensate for neurological glitches rather than making the secondary zone-disordered child listen until he can process! This concept will be revisited in assessment and intervention chapters later in this book, but it is important food for thought at this point.

In conclusion, the Processing Continuum Model defines brain areas that are responsible for processing auditory stimuli. In the past, audiologists' orientation has been neurological, while speech-language pathologists' orientation has been behavioral. The neuropsychological Processing Continuum Model imposes neurology on the observed behaviors to imply brain function in a hierarchical progression. This model provides a very clear structure to design assessment and intervention for processing disorders.

Functional Units Outline

Anatomy & Physiology of the Language Processing System

A. First functional unit—reticular formation (midbrain, pons, & medulla oblongata)

　　1. Neurological readiness to interact with environment

　　2. Energy system for cortex

　　3. Directs sensorineural traffic

　　4. Awakens brain; keeps it alert

　　5. Maintains attentive state to incoming signals

B. Second functional unit—parietal, occipital, & temporal lobes

　　1. Isolate neural impulses into discrete areas for analysis

　　　　a. Visual stimuli—occipital

　　　　b. Tactile stimuli—parietal

　　　　c. Auditory stimuli—temporal

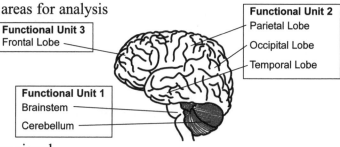

　　2. Each lobe divided into 3 zones

　　　　a. Primary zone—sensory sensation

　　　　　　(1) Reception of incoming sensory signal

　　　　　　(2) Sensation of signal rather than extensive processing

　　　　b. Secondary zone—attach meaning

　　　　　　(1) Process incoming information

　　　　　　(2) Interpretation through coding, organizing, associating, & storing

　　　　　　(3) Integrate into meaningful experiences/information

　　　　c. Tertiary zone—integration

　　　　　　(1) Integrate new information with old stored information

　　　　　　(2) Integrate discrete sensory impulses across sensory modalities

　　　　　　(3) Integrate information from all cortices for higher level processing

　　　　　　(4) Transfer from passive receptive to active expressive response

C. Third functional unit—frontal lobes

　　1. Active response through motoric expression

　　2. Planning and managing behavior

Chapter 3: Quick Quiz Questions

Identify the following as occurring in the first (**1**), second (**2**), or third (**3**) functional units.

1. _____ Planning and managing an individual's behavior

2. _____ Consists of brainstem structures

3. _____ Responsible for neurological alertness/readiness

4. _____ Further divided into three zones

5. _____ Involved in processing by association, coding, and organizing

6. _____ Responsible for an expressive output or response

7. _____ Consists of temporal, occipital, and parietal lobes

8. _____ Consists of the frontal lobes

9. _____ Serves as the sensory screener for incoming stimuli

Identify the following as representing the primary (**P**), secondary (**S**), or tertiary (**T**) zone of the second functional unit, temporal lobe.

10. _____ Receives sensory sensation

11. _____ Integrates new information with information stored previously

12. _____ Association area

13. _____ Heschl's gyrus

14. _____ Angular gyrus

15. _____ Primary site for reading

16. _____ Primary site for language processing

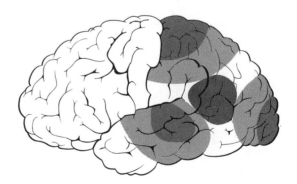

(Answers are on page 184.)

Student Examples of Processing Disorders

Before we compile a list of specific behavioral characteristics of children with processing deficits, let's first visit a few functional examples of students, compliments of *Peanuts, Calvin & Hobbs,* and other cartoonist friends. See if you recognize any of your students in these examples!

This is an example of learning to play the teacher's game without understanding the reasons. Many children try to please a teacher by performing a task or going through the motions as directed, but learning has not occurred.

Students are often chastised for not following instructions, but it isn't always their fault. Stop in a classroom sometime and listen to teacher directions. Sometimes the language of instruction is one long sentence that far exceeds a child's short-term memory loop. Without visual backup, children with processing problems have little hope of completing the right tasks.

Information moves through the neurological system more slowly for children with processing disorders. Sometimes it takes much longer for them to attach meaning to an auditory stimulus, resulting in a latency when compared to the pace of the normal classroom. Quite often their efforts to continue processing questions are not rewarded, which can result in the next behavior.

When auditory information comes fast and furious in a classroom setting, it can become overwhelming to a child with processing problems. It is easier to daydream or "check-out" than to try to keep up.

PEANUTS © Schulz. Reprinted with permission of United Media. All rights reserved.

Children with processing deficits can have meaning mapped onto a vocabulary term; the problem is that the meaning can change based on the situation. *Omen* and *sign* are synonyms in many contexts, but not in baseball. Signs are a very normal part of the game, while superstitions and routine rituals abound to bring good luck; omens are not necessarily a good thing!

Children with processing disorders can be quite verbal. That doesn't mean that they say much. It would be very difficult to answer any questions from this sports report because no specific content is included. It is all generic, empty language terms.

Phonemic confusion is becoming a landmark feature of processing disorders. Many words that are similar in their phonemic construction have very different meanings.

Give these students credit for creativity! Despite the processing deficits, they can truly enjoy language and playing with terminology, often creating new words that mean something to them but confuse the rest of us!

Colloquial language is a challenge to everyone. Trying to stay current on word use confounds the best of us! Remember when *bad* was negative, as opposed to *good*? No wonder children with processing problems get lost in the dust!

Words can have multiple meanings. For a child who just visited Disneyland, *Pluto* evokes memories of pictures taken with the Disney dog. The child will write a very strange report about a *space probe landing on Pluto* if this is the picture in his mind!

Beetle Bailey

Problems with humor, irony, puns, etc., are common with processing disorders. The abstract meanings of words stretch beyond the processing level of complexity for some children with deficits in processing.

Students with processing problems often become so wrapped up in other aspects of an experience, they forget the basic facts. Add the latency and other confusions that accompany processing deficits, and the result is frequently muttering "I forgot." We all experience this phenomenon and know how frustrating it can be.

A teaching presentation style that seems straightforword and clear to some students can be a complete mystery to a child with processing problems. Teachers' obscure questions don't provide these students with enough information to retrieve the knowledge they have. Poor performance on quizzes is more often a reflection of poor question format than it is of student learning.

Grades can be a mystery to children with processing disorders. While the teacher observes daydreaming, confusion, latency in responses, and frequent "I don't know" or "I forgot" comments from a student, the student does have the knowledge and often understands information—at his own pace. Consequently, when the student brings a poor report card home and his parents are upset, the student is baffled. He insists that he doesn't know how he got those grades—he understood everything!

Children with processing problems can present significant challenges to a teacher. They deal with information in a different way and often view the world from their own perspectives to make sense of it. But that doesn't have to make them shy or retiring!

Impulsive responses and jumping to conclusions are not uncommon with processing disorders. Children receive a distorted signal and impulsively respond to it before they have all the information.

Enthusiasm for social interaction and participation can be significantly marred by processing deficits. Sincere attempts sometimes fail miserably.

```
┌─────────────────┐      ┌─────────────────────┐
│      Rick       │      │       Marla         │
│      for        │      │        for          │
│   President     │      │   Half-President    │
└─────────────────┘      └─────────────────────┘
```

Poor processing can result in peer pragmatic problems. A well-intentioned action can trigger humiliation due to inappropriate actions. Election posters all over the school announcing candidacy for "half-president" instead of "vice-president" will probably not instill confidence in peers.

Some children try so hard—but still can't get it right.

Did you recognize characteristics from a few of the processing disordered students you have encountered? The trick is to sort out central auditory processing behaviors from language processing behaviors. Obviously there will be some overlap, but differences based on the neurological models presented in previous chapters help to differentiate between the two disorders.

Central Auditory Processing Problems

Central auditory processing disorders (CAPD) entail a deficit in the auditory pathways of the brain that results in the inability to listen to or comprehend auditory information accurately even though normal intelligence and hearing sensitivity are documented (Keith, 1986). Keith suggests that children with CAPD generally exist as a subset of children with language and learning difficulties. In other words, the central auditory processing problem can be one part of a continuum of problems.

A variety of lists define characteristics observed in children with auditory processing problems. Some focus on defining the skills or auditory tasks that present difficulty for children with central auditory processing problems. Others focus on the observed behaviors that might appear different as a result of the CANS deficit. The actual skills will be delineated in the next chapter dealing with assessment. The current chapter discusses the behaviors observed in the home or school environments that indicate possible problems in the CANS.

After reviewing multiple resources, I compiled a list of twelve behaviors that were primary in most resources for CAPD (see page 53). A more detailed description of each behavioral item is given below. Some of the resource information was generated when central auditory processing and language processing disorders were grouped together under the label of *auditory processing disorders*. In my list, I attempted to differentiate between the characteristics of central auditory processing disorders vs. language processing disorders; a list of characteristics of language processing disorders follows this information about CAPD. Although some overlap exists between the two lists of disorder characteristics, the reasons prompting the behaviors are different.

It is unlikely that any one child will match all the characteristics. The list includes the highest frequency items, as reported by a number of different professionals over time. These items serve as a checklist to determine if parents or professionals suspect central auditory processing problems, resulting in referral for assessment. The checklist is also part of the reproducible form on page 69; you may reproduce this checklist as often as necessary for your students or clients.

1. Majority are male (75%)

Gender differences in brain development and function are consistently reported in the literature. Exposure to male hormones during embryonic development appears to affect the structural, physiological, and biochemical organization of the brain. Clinical studies have suggested "selective vulnerability of left hemisphere structures, particularly the temporal lobe, in males" (Keith, 1982). Neurological maturation, including the myelinization

(continued on page 54)

Characteristics of Central Auditory Processing Disorders

1. Majority are male (75%)

2. Normal pure-tone hearing results

3. Difficulty following oral directions; inconsistent response to auditory stimuli

4. Short auditory attention span; fatigues easily during auditory tasks

5. Poor short-term and long-term memory

6. Gives impression of not listening even though looking at the speaker; daydreams

7. Difficulty listening in presence of background noise

8. Difficulty localizing sound

9. Academic deficits (phonics, reading, or spelling) and mild speech-language impairments

10. Disruptive behaviors—distracted, impulsive, frustrated

11. Frequent requests for verbal repetition or often saying "huh?"

12. History of otitis media

process, can be significantly slower in males. Normal maturation of the CANS system is generally thought to take as long as seven years. All these factors account for the fact that approximately two-thirds of children diagnosed with CAPD are male.

2. Normal pure-tone hearing results

Evaluation results of the peripheral auditory system generally show normal auditory acuity. Numerous studies over the years have consistently demonstrated that children with CAPD do not usually have significant hearing loss. In fact, normal to near-normal bilateral hearing levels are required to adequately assess the central auditory nervous system. The premise of a CAP disorder is that the signal has been adequately received by the peripheral auditory system, but it becomes compromised or distorted during the neurological transference to the cortex.

3. Difficulty following oral directions; inconsistent responses to auditory stimuli

Children with CAPD sometimes respond very appropriately to auditory stimuli, but at other times, they don't respond at all or appear to be very confused by what is being said. The speaker observes the child ignoring or partially following a direction and might become angry. It is important for the speaker to realize that the child probably didn't receive an intact auditory message. It's hard to comply with what you didn't hear! What exasperates parents and teachers is the inconsistency. Because the auditory stimuli sometimes make it to the cortex, the inappropriate responses are variable and often interpreted as manipulative avoidance behavior rather than a legitimate problem. Children with CAPD often listen very attentively and carefully, but they simply can't follow long or complicated verbal directions. The behavior observed can appear to be a frequent misunderstanding of directions or information.

4. Short auditory attention span; fatigues easily during auditory tasks

When auditory signals are being distorted or compromised before the cortex "hears" them, the effort to pay attention is very tiring and effortful! As the auditory signal increases in length and complexity, the challenge to fill-in missing or distorted components of the signal requires incredible energy and focus. The auditory channel is not the strongest learning channel for children with CAPD. They tend to rely on visual and physical demonstration to supplement auditory presentation.

If you have ever visited a foreign country where you had a beginner's knowledge of the language, you realize how carefully you had to listen, and even then, you only picked up major words and ideas. The effort to remain coherent zaps your energy quickly. That scenario is what a child with CAPD endures on a daily basis. When a teacher or parent talks for an extended period of time without offering supplement cues, a child with CAPD quickly loses attention due to the sustained effort required.

5. Poor short-term and long-term memory

When auditory stimuli are not being received intact, the child's immediate need is to fill-in and make sense of the signal. The energy channeled into interpreting the signal can minimize the amount of auditory attention available for memory, both long and short term. The child impulsively tries to figure out what the auditory signal is, not always listening to or receiving the entire stimulus. That is why short-term memory is negatively effected; the child isn't able to relax and listen to the entire signal before having to begin working on the information.

A shortened or distorted signal isn't likely to be processed adequately for storage in long-term memory. Only rudimentary knowledge might be applied to the auditory stimulus, compromising what is stored in long-term memory for later retrieval. Other ways that the memory deficits can be evidenced would be trouble remembering things like days of the week, months of the year, address and phone number, and the alphabet.

6. Gives impression of not listening even though looking at the speaker; daydreams

Teachers and parents describe children with CAPD as having trouble getting started on tasks or not paying attention when directions are given. The children often appear to be looking right at the speaker, but their eyes glaze over and they seem to be daydreaming. What prompts this behavior? The children quickly become overwhelmed by the verbal message since it is distorted, faint, partially received, etc., due to the deficit CANS. Once the auditory stimuli become a blur of noise, the children retreat to their own world of daydreams, which they can control and make sense of. Another strategy is to ignore the speaker since the message doesn't make any sense.

7. Difficulty listening in presence of background noise

When a child has a CAN deficit, listening to auditory stimuli can be exhausting, even in the best auditory environment. When the surroundings become noisy or distracting, listening can be next to impossible. Individuals with hearing impairments or who wear hearing aids can attest to this phenomenon.

I am deaf in one ear with very good hearing in the other. In a noisy environment, I have to supplement much of the auditory signal with lip reading and contextual closure by guessing what might have been said. The primary auditory signal is accompanied by a multitude of other auditory noises and stimuli, making listening an exhausting task. I never stay very long at large gatherings; it's too frustrating and exhausting! Children who are trying to listen and learn in a noisy academic environment experience the same problems, frustrations, and reaction—they mentally leave the room!

8. Difficulty localizing sound

Knowing which direction a sound comes from requires receiving a fairly intact signal. A child puts a lot of effort into trying to piece together a distorted message, using all the internal and external redundancies possible. It isn't always possible to determine the primary source of the sound or to know its importance when trying to understand the content within the signal. Children with central auditory processing problems can have difficulty determining the distance of sounds, how close or far the source of a signal is, as well as the loudness of sounds. Because children with CAPD can't always process the nuances of a signal, some react in a very sensitive manner to loud noises or auditory stimuli they can't control or that might startle their systems.

9. Academic deficits (phonics, reading, or spelling) and mild speech-language impairments

Most children with "pure" CAPD do not necessarily have speech-language impairments. The typical problem in CAPD is mild articulation impairment due to distorted speech signals. Other areas of deficit involve discerning acoustic features of the auditory stimulus, such as phonemic synthesis, auditory figure-ground, sound discrimination, and so forth. The phonemic deficits can secondarily impact reading, spelling, and foundation skills for more complex academic areas.

Certainly when auditory signals are distorted, the risk of misunderstanding information increases, yet if cues or accommodations are provided to compensate for the impaired auditory signal, language processing deficits can be prevented. An impairment in the CANS does not necessarily mean that cortical language abilities will be impaired.

10. Disruptive behaviors—distracted, impulsive, frustrated

Children with CAPD are trying to cope with distorted acoustic stimuli on a regular basis. The frustration of trying to make sense of our very auditory world, usually presented at a rapid pace, can cause incredible frustration, which can result in a variety of atypical behavioral responses, depending on the personality of the child.

Some children become easily distracted due to the constant barrage of inaccurate auditory signals they receive. Others respond impulsively, hoping to avoid having to process or listen to an entire distorted message; they respond quickly to the first aspect of the message that makes sense to them. While a large percentage of children act out their frustration overtly, some children withdraw and interact only minimally with others to limit their chances of responding inaccurately.

11. Frequent requests for verbal repetition or often saying "huh?"

A child with problems in the CANS is not receiving intact auditory stimuli in the cortex. Consequently, it is very difficult for him to attach meaning and act on the information. Rather than try to re-assemble or fill in the messed up signal, it is easier to just ask that it be repeated and hope the repeated stimulus makes it through the auditory brainstem to the cortex this time. Sometimes the child has received part of the signal and wants to hear it again to try to catch the remainder. Another reason children say "huh?" is to provide additional time to figure out the signal or to provide a check through the repetition to see if what they heard was accurate.

Paula Tallal's work has also suggested that temporal and sequential aspects of an auditory stimulus are impaired in children with processing disorders. This deficit results in a latency for processing the acoustic features of the signal, and the child develops strategies to buy more time.

12. History of otitis media

Research has suggested that many children with CAPD have a positive medical history for frequent middle-ear infections, tubes, and antibiotic use during early childhood. Chronic otitis media may indicate structural developmental differences, serving as a warning sign for similar subtle differences in the central auditory nervous system.

Other miscellaneous characteristics

Several authors included soft neurological signs as an additional possible indicator of CAPD. Items classified under this heading included conditions such as allergies, poor motor coordination, attention deficit hyperactivity disorder, and abnormal EEGs. However, none of them were strongly supported or appeared to be significant as an at-risk feature for central auditory processing disorders.

Language Processing Problems

Language processing disorders (LPD) describe a deficit in the cortex of the brain that results in the inability to attach increasingly complex layers of meaning to an auditory stimulus, even though the signal is received intactly and normal intelligence and general language foundation skills are age commensurate. As with CAPD, language processing disorders usually exist as a subset of children diagnosed with learning disabilities. In fact, 80% of learning disabilities are founded in language difficulties, quite often language processing disorders.

The common characteristics for LPD, listed in the box on page 59, are based on a checklist of behaviors used to identify students at risk for language processing disorders that was published in the *Language Processing Kit (*Richard & Hanner, 1995). That checklist was designed to be completed by teachers to result in referrals for students who should be further evaluated in the area of language processing. A frequency of occurrence was applied to each of the behaviors observed to help determine if the behavioral profile was cause for concern.

The checklist has been modified and adapted to correspond with the format used previously in this chapter for CAPD, as well as to reflect current research findings. Each item included on the list is further explained below. The list is not necessarily inclusive, nor is any one child with language processing deficits expected to evidence all of the characteristics. As with the CAPD list, the LPD list reflects the high frequency items reported consistently by professionals over time. The list should serve as a checklist to help parents and professionals determine if language processing deficits are suspected so that appropriate referrals for testing can occur (see the CAPD/LPD Checklist, page 69).

1. Problems with retrieval of common words

One of the most frequently reported characteristics in language processing disorders is word retrieval problems. Children often struggle to retrieve common everyday labels. A third-grade boy asked to leave therapy early to go meet "that lady." We weren't about to let him go until we knew whom he was supposed to meet. After extensive struggle, we figured out it was his mom! The important aspect to understand in word retrieval deficits is that the language term is in there—somewhere. The problem is not retrieval if the vocabulary term hasn't been learned. This concept will be developed later, but it is critical for teachers to understand. Compensating for word retrieval is not giving answers; it is facilitating retrieval of stored information. If the student really doesn't have the knowledge, then the problem is a language acquisition problem.

Characteristics of Language Processing Disorders

1. Problems with retrieval of common words

2. Use of neutral, generic, or less-specific labels

3. Misuse of words with a similar phonetic structure

4. Generating creative, original language terms; use of descriptions or circumlocutions

5. Response latency; use of fillers to buy time

6. Frequent "I don't know" or "I forgot" responses

7. Verbal repetition or rehearsal

8. Inconsistency in learning; requires extensive review of previously-learned material

9. Recognizes language errors but can't fix them

10. Incomplete sentences or thoughts

11. Pragmatic problems; disruptive behavior

12. Age-commensurate IQ and vocabulary with academic deficits; *learning disability* label

2. Use of neutral, generic, or less-specific labels

Due to retrieval problems, children with language processing problems rely on general terms to express themselves and hope the listener will fill in specific context. Generic terms can apply to a number of situations without being inaccurate. A child might want to go to the zoo "to see animals" rather than naming specific animals of interest. This problem creates confusion when the terms used become too generic. If you ask what a child wants to have for lunch, a response of *food* is a bit too general. Children with LPD often use category labels rather than specific noun labels. Also watch for frequent use of non-specific words, such as *thing* and *stuff*.

3. Misuse of words with a similar phonetic structure

Children with LPD often use words with a similar phonetic structure incorrectly. A child in therapy kept talking about smiling *on* the mirror rather than *in* the mirror, which confused the listener.

A word used in error can also be similar by associative context. The cartoon in the Preface (page 5) illustrates a significant functional outcome when the antonym pair of *off/on* was confused, resulting in the wrong kind of insect repellent.

4. Generating creative, original language terms; use of descriptions or circumlocutions

When a specific term eludes a child, the desire to express his thought might lead to creating new words. One little boy told me about feeding the "quacking birds" at the park. His description allowed me to think *duck*, but his descriptive words wouldn't gain any points on a vocabulary test. Teachers often become frustrated when students go on and on when one or two words would have been sufficient. One primary student got in trouble for asking to borrow a pencil. The problem was not the request; it was how he asked. He couldn't pull the word *pencil,* so he went into a long tangent about "the yellow stick that you write with, put in that thing over there and turn the handle to make it real pointed," etc. His circumlocution all around the word held up the class spelling test for longer than the teacher was willing to wait.

5. Response latency; use of fillers to buy time

Moving language through the cortex for processing, zone by zone, until a response can be programmed takes time for children with LPD. If you take too long to respond, someone else generally takes control of the conversation, and you lose your turn. Some children keep the conversational floor with *you know, um, like,* and other fillers to keep their turn until they have completed attaching meaning to the message to formulate a response. One little girl, who had a left temporal lobe lesion due to a seizure at age four, had a significant latency. Occasionally I had to wait 60-90 seconds for her response! I sometimes forgot my question by the time she responded. The hardest part was to sit quietly and wait without generating more verbal stimuli for her to process.

6. Frequent "I don't know" or "I forgot" response

The normal question-response latency time is two-to-four seconds. That isn't long enough for children with language processing problems. When more time is required, students become anxious about holding up the class. Rather than have negative peer pressure weighing down their processing, they respond with *I don't know.* In the classroom, the pressure is off as the teacher moves on to someone else. What the teacher fails to realize is that the student may indeed know the answer, but not in the time expected.

7. Verbal repetition or rehearsal

Children with LPD are frequently caught mumbling to themselves or "talking." In fact, they are trying to keep the auditory stimulus fresh in short-term memory until they can decode it or get meaning attached to it. They are actually demonstrating a great compensatory strategy that is advocated later in the remediation section of this book. However, teachers sometimes view this behavior as distracting or disruptive and sabotage these students' language processing efforts.

8. Inconsistency in learning; requires extensive review of previously-learned material

The learning process can be exasperating for children with language processing disorders and their teachers. When information is presented with lots of examples and demonstration, these students are probably focused and participating with understanding. The problem is, that new knowledge might not get stored in a very organized manner, if at all, to retrieve and use again the next day. The teacher discovers that the content has to be taught all over again or requires extensive review to reach the place they were yesterday to begin adding new information to it. The problem is one of organized storage into long-term memory for later language use. The integration of new and old information doesn't go smoothly!

9. Recognizes language errors but can't fix them

When a teacher provides feedback to a student with language processing problems, the student usually recognizes the error but doesn't know how to correct it. This is one reason I tend to group language processing students for therapy. They can actually learn to better understand and recognize their own errors from perceiving them in other students. Discriminating problems is the first step toward implementing a remediation strategy.

10. Incomplete sentences or thoughts

A conversation with someone who has language processing deficits can be a challenging endeavor. Sentences may never be finished; they hang out there for the listener to complete, clarify, or fill in. Disjointed pieces of information have meaning to the student, but the context isn't always shared very effectively with the listener to facilitate his or her processing. The same pattern can be present in written language.

11. Pragmatic problems; disruptive behavior

Disruptive, inappropriate behavior is a frequent secondary characteristic of LPD. Research shows that the majority of juvenile delinquents and students who drop out of school have undiagnosed language processing and/or language-learning problems. The frustration of being made to feel stupid when you have the language knowledge but can't access it in the typical school structure leads to aggressive outbursts and disruptive behavior in many students.

The other extreme is to become very withdrawn, depressed, and internal to avoid the ridicule of peers making fun of your unsuccessful academic attempts. The rules for social interaction are subtle and often revolve around plays on words, teasing comments, and other abstract uses of language. The nuances of pragmatic language that are supposed to occur in different social situations are simply too mystical for children with LPD to make sense of. One strategy is to become the class clown and purposely draw the attention in a controlled way before it becomes uncontrolled negative attention leveled by a teacher or a peer.

12. Age-commensurate IQ and vocabulary with academic deficits; learning disability label

"Pure" language processing disorders occur with relatively normal measures of intellectual and academic potential. If anything, performance will be in the low average range, but the "Swiss cheese" pattern indicates an uneven language foundation that tends to collapse as academic language demands increase over time. Parents and teachers express frustration when a student's potential measures in a normal range, but his day-to-day classroom performance doesn't reflect that level of output. The immediate reaction is to blame the student for not applying himself. Schools resist using a *learning disability* label and gravitate toward a *behavior* or *emotional disability* label, putting the deficits in a behavioral interpretation rather than a neurological framework.

Preschool Precursory Behavioral Profile for Processing Problems

Research evidence is indisputable that early intervention makes a difference! One of the problems in the educational setting decades ago was that a learning disability couldn't be diagnosed until a two-year academic discrepancy existed, meaning that a child couldn't receive services prior to second grade. By that time, a student was already significantly behind peers in academic performance, and learning disabilities became a life sentence with the child rarely, if ever, catching up.

Clinical studies over time have indicated that preschool children can evidence a profile of language behaviors that suggest a likelihood for language processing problems. It is difficult to diagnose language processing problems during the preschool years because the language foundation that processing will scaffold on is being laid. Language processing presumes developmental language abilities that are age-commensurate in phonology, syntax and morphology, semantics, and pragmatics. Basic vocabulary knowledge has to be acquired before a child can attach more in-depth meaning to it. However, the pattern a child demonstrates as she acquires her language foundation can raise a yellow flag of caution, signaling that the child is at risk for a language processing disorder.

Eight characteristics have consistently emerged as the warning signs of possible future language processing deficits. A child doesn't have to demonstrate all eight language problems before a speech-language pathologist becomes concerned. I use this rule of thumb: if I substantiate more than five of the language behaviors during an evaluation on a preschool child, then I usually recommend speech-language services. Getting an early start may prevent later language-learning problems.

The language problems can be observed informally. The speech-language pathologist should not wait until the characteristics can be documented on formal standardized assessment. Again, this approach loses key early intervention time to prevent language weaknesses from escalating into more significant problems.

Preschool Precursors for Language Processing Problems

1. Poor sequencing in both receptive and expressive language
2. Slow acquisition of vocabulary and concepts
3. Ineffective short-term memory
4. Slow receptive and expressive acquisition of *Wh-* question forms
5. Delayed articulation/phonological development
6. Significant word retrieval problems
7. Slow syntactic development with persistent error patterns
8. Slow pragmatic development with poor awareness of conversational rules

1. Poor sequencing in both receptive and expressive language

Poor verbal organization can be a significant signal for language processing problems. How is this demonstrated in a preschool child? Ask him about the Disney movie he just saw. He might tell you the ending, then the plot, then the characters, then something from the beginning, etc. If you find yourself asking lots of questions to sort out the sequence, then you have just experienced poor expressive sequencing skills. Receptive sequencing would be shown if a child has trouble learning things in order, such as the child's address, phone number, rote counting, and the alphabet.

2. Slow acquisition of vocabulary and concepts

Delayed vocabulary and concept acquisition are relatively easy to spot on a receptive or expressive vocabulary test, such as the *Peabody Picture Vocabulary Test* or the *Receptive/ Expressive One Word Picture Vocabulary Test.* A child with a language processing disorder may drive you crazy as you try to secure a basal and ceiling. You start at what you think is an appropriate level, but you can't get a basal until you have gone all the way back to the beginning. As you work toward a ceiling, the child is getting tired. You count in your head and think *one more,* but the child gets it right, so you have to go on. After more bribes, you think you have a ceiling again—only to have the child pull one out, so you have to keep going. It seems like you go on forever and feel pretty good as the child is now way above her age. When you score the test later, there are so many errors that the child's performance comes out low average or borderline.

What emerges is a "Swiss cheese" pattern of language development. Language is scattered across the age range but is very inconsistent in the developmental pattern. The child's acquisition of language is spotty and prevents her from having a solid foundation upon which to build. Remember that language processing is attaching increasingly complex meaning to vocabulary terms. If concrete nouns are not established, the child can't attach more in-depth knowledge to them.

3. Ineffective short-term memory

Parents and teachers speak with frustration about the child who "can't remember anything." In a preschool child, a typical scenario is being given a direction but only remembering part of it. The functional result can be exasperating. Dad might say, "Go up to your room and get a sweater; we're leaving for Grandma's house." The child runs to his room, and then yells, "What am I supposed to get?" Another example is when a preschool teacher introduces a concept and the child gets it perfect, but the next day, it's like it was never taught. Short-term memory is also called *working memory*. Duration is usually for 5-20 seconds. A child with short-memory problems isn't able to hang on to information long enough to process, or attach meaning to it. If a child can't retain information in short-term memory long enough to work on the message, certainly he is at risk for processing problems later.

4. Slow receptive and expressive acquisition of *Wh-* question forms

Children at risk for processing deficits struggle with development of *Wh*-question forms. Weak comprehension is apparent when a child is asked a question and he answers, but with the wrong information. For example, a parent asks the child what he would like for lunch, and he answers with where he wants to go ("McDonald's") without trying to manipulate a trip to the restaurant.

The confusion also shows up when the child asks an adult a question. Once answered, the child gets angry and asks it again. Usually the problem is that the child chose the wrong *Wh-* question form and isn't getting the information desired.

5. Delayed articulation/phonological development

Children at risk for processing deficits do not present significant concerns in the area of sound acquisition. They are generally intelligible and not significantly disordered when evaluated with standardized or informal assessment techniques. However, sound errors are present in a borderline range of severity.

The other major characteristic noted in this area is a dramatic discrepancy between single-word articulation and connected speech. Usually there is a noticeable difference in the ability to produce single words (fairly appropriate) and to be understood during spontaneous conversation (poor intelligibility). It is important to evaluate using more than single-word naming tests to detect this discrepancy.

6. Significant word retrieval problems

When children use a lot of generic language, warning lights should start flashing! On expressive vocabulary tests and even articulation tests, the children struggle to retrieve common item labels, even though the examiner feels they know what the objects are. An informal way to pick up on this characteristic is to pay attention to how many questions an adult must ask to make sense of information a preschool child is trying to share. If the child is talking a mile a minute but all the details must be filled in by an adult asking clarification questions, then probably the content words are missing.

7. Slow syntactic development with persistent error patterns

Despite the time involved, a spontaneous language sample is important during preschool evaluations. The development of syntax can mirror the "Swiss cheese" pattern of semantic acquisition, with holes and inconsistencies. One of the best ways to determine that is by completing a syntactic analysis to illustrate irregularities in the developmental pattern, as well as immaturity of sentence structures. Key syntax aspects to look for are included in the list at the top of the following page.

- reduced mean length of utterance (MLU)

- word order confusion

- restricted diversity in word use; low type-token ration (TTR)

- simple sentence structure rather than complex syntactic forms

- inconsistent syntactic forms, i.e., uses high-level structures with errors in early-developing structures

8. Slow pragmatic development; poor awareness of conversational rules

Children at risk for processing deficits are social and interact with other people, but they don't always do it very well. They tend to interrupt, jump from topic to topic, and assume the speaker has knowledge that hasn't been shared. In a preschool setting, they may be in trouble frequently for not following implied social rules. They often act more immature than their chronological age suggests.

These eight characteristics just described have a domino effect on academic learning, as charted and explained below.

Academic Skill Progression	Characteristic Impacting Skill Development							
	1	2	3	4	5	6	7	8
Rote Alphabet	X	X	X			X		
Sound-Symbol Correspondence	X	X	X		X	X		
Oral Reading	X	X	X		X	X	X	
Reading Comprehension	X	X	X	X	X	X	X	
Workbook Tasks	X	X	X	X	X	X	X	X
Written Language	X	X	X	X	X	X	X	X

The first area of observed deficit will be difficulty when trying to learn the letter names of the alphabet. Four of the eight deficits are already contributing to difficulties encountered in this task—sequencing, vocabulary acquisition, short-term memory problems, and word retrieval. The academic skill that builds on the rote alphabet letters is sound-symbol correspondence. A fifth deficit is added to the mix, articulation/phonology problems. The next academic skill that builds on sound-symbol correspondence is oral reading, where a sixth characteristic of delayed syntax skills further compounds learning. From oral reading, academic tasks progress into reading comprehension, where *Wh-* question form confusion complicates matters. The next academic level will be worksheet tasks, where the final characteristic of pragmatic language comes into play. The child is constantly at the teacher's desk asking questions, seeking clarification, and driving adults in the room crazy. By the time written language skills are being developed, all eight deficits are working against the child to prevent effective learning.

Another factor of importance is the pace of academic expectations in schools today. It used to be that in kindergarten, basic concepts, colors, numbers, etc., were introduced. Now parents are given a list of prerequisite skills a child must have mastered before enrolling in kindergarten. Preschool is no longer an option; it is a requirement.

The problem with these expectations is that schools are beginning to violate normal neurological maturation. Most children's neurological systems are not ready to read at age five. The auditory nervous system is still myelinating through age seven, yet teachers expect full and accurate speech discrimination and sound-symbol correspondence to be in place prior to enrollment in kindergarten. School curriculum committees need to carefully evaluate academic expectations in light of the neurological evidence for processing and learning. In many cases, schools are creating learning difficulties and disabilities by setting neurologically impossible standards!

Behavior Checklists

Because processing disorders can be subtle, it is important to routinely complete checklists on students in preschool and the primary grades to pick up processing deficits before they turn into academic or behavior problems. The Checklist for Processing Difficulties on page 69 serves as a checklist for both central auditory processing and language processing deficits. The Preschool Checklist for Processing Difficulties on page 70 is a checklist for preschoolers who may be at risk for processing deficits.

Checklist for Processing Difficulties

Child's name _____ Age _____ School _____

Parent/Guardian _____ Recorder _____ Date _____

Check all items that apply to the child. Note comments below.

Central Auditory Processing

_____ Male

_____ Normal pure-tone hearing

_____ Difficulty following oral directions; inconsistent responses

_____ Short auditory attention span; fatigues easily

_____ Poor short-term and long-term memory

_____ Daydreams; appears not to listen

_____ Difficulty hearing with background noise

_____ Difficulty localizing sounds

_____ Academic and/or speech-language problems

_____ Disruptive behaviors; impulsive, frustrated

_____ Requests repetition; asks "huh?"

_____ History of ear infections

Language Processing

_____ Word retrieval problems

_____ Neutral, generic language

_____ Misuse of words with a similar phonetic structure

_____ Creative, original language; describes or circumlocutes

_____ Delayed responses; uses fillers

_____ Frequently answers "I don't know" or "I forgot"

_____ Repeats or rehearses comments

_____ Inconsistency in learning; needs review

_____ Recognizes errors but can't correct them

_____ Incomplete sentences or thoughts

_____ Pragmatic problems; disruptive behavior

_____ Age-appropriate IQ and vocabulary; academic deficits; learning disabled

Comments:

_____

_____

_____

Preschool Checklist for Processing Difficulties

Child's name _____ Age _____ Preschool _____

Parent/Guardian _____ Recorder _____ Date _____

Check all items that apply to the child. Note comments below.

_____ 1. Poor sequencing in both receptive and expressive language

_____ 2. Slow development of vocabulary and concepts

_____ 3. Ineffective short-term memory

_____ 4. Slow development in understanding and using *Wh-* questions

_____ 5. Delayed articulation or phonological development (speech sounds)

_____ 6. Significant word retrieval problems

_____ 7. Immature grammar with persistent error patterns

_____ 8. Slow to develop social language skills; poor awareness of conversation rules

Comments

_____

_____

_____

_____

_____

_____

_____

Chapter 5: Processing Assessment

Assessment of processing disorders is multifaceted and has divided responsibilities among the professions of audiology and speech-language pathology. The continuum of processing, established through the models of central auditory processing and language processing in earlier chapters, delineates a neurological model that mediates the behaviors evaluated in processing assessment.

Thorough assessment for processing deficits must carefully evaluate the hierarchy of processing to determine the neurological level of breakdown. Effective intervention is based on accurate diagnosis. If assessment is not carefully controlled, then intervention resorts to "hit and miss" therapy based on subtest performance rather than the substantiated neurological aspects of a deficit.

This chapter will progress through the hierarchy suggested in the Processing Continuum Model. Central auditory processing assessment is the responsibility of audiologists; language processing is the responsibility of speech-language pathologists. The overlap area is defined by auditory skill areas and can be assessed by either audiologists or speech-language pathologists. The best assessment procedures are usually co-disciplinary with input from the fields of both audiology and speech-language pathology.

The Processing Continuum Model

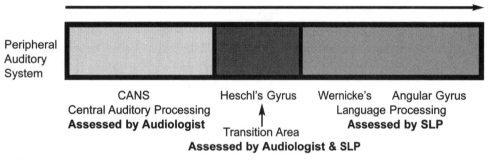

While audiologists are responsible for central auditory processing (CAP) assessment, speech-language pathologists are usually charged with providing remediation for central auditory processing disorders (CAPD). For this reason, it is important for speech-language pathologists to understand the basic principles of audiometric assessment of the central auditory nervous system. An SLP will need to make sense of audiometric test results to determine appropriate intervention strategies and goals. An audiologist usually includes recommendations based on assessment results, but an SLP is typically the professional who has to insure compliance with those recommendations in an educational setting.

Central Auditory Processing Assessment

Purpose of Central Auditory Processing Assessment

Tests to evaluate for CAPD are generally divided into the categories of *audiological* and *non-audiological assessment instruments*. Audiological assessment covers the central auditory nervous system (brainstem), and non-audiological assessment addresses cortical Heschl's gyrus abilities, or the overlap area. This section deals with the audiological assessment procedures for CAPD, evaluating the integrity of CANS.

The underlying premise for central auditory processing assessment is outlined below.

- The brain looks for consistency in processing auditory signals.

- Auditory pathways are redundant, so the normal listener can tolerate a degree of variability in a signal by using a constructive process to fill-in signal deficiencies.

- If a signal is confusing, then an abnormal behavioral response will occur.

- An abnormal response indicates a problem related to the internal or external redundancy within the auditory nervous system.

Based on these assumptions, the purpose of central auditory processing testing is to assess the neurological integrity of the brainstem and initial cortical structures for intact transmission of acoustic stimuli. The CAP tests must stress or challenge the central auditory nervous system as it tries to process an acoustic stimulus. This challenge is accomplished by eliminating or reducing the redundancy or by compromising the acoustic signal.

Prerequisites for CAP Assessment

To adequately evaluate the CANS, three requirements must be met:

1. Normal/near normal auditory peripheral hearing
2. Adequate receptive/expressive language acquisition
3. Normal/near normal intellectual function

If we follow the processing continuum model, evaluation of the auditory peripheral system is prerequisite to assessment of the CANS. For central auditory processing assessment, the child must have bilateral hearing levels that are not significantly compromised. Volume modifications can compensate for a degree of conductive hearing loss, but fairly equal hearing acuity is necessary to adequately assess the integrity of the post-peripheral auditory system. The premise of CAP assessment is based on internal and external redundancy in the CANS. If redundancy or signal integrity is already compromised before it reaches the eighth auditory nerve for neurological transfer, then it will be very difficult to evaluate integrity of CANS through audiological procedures. Peripheral assessment should precede any CAP tests and should include pure-tone audiometry, speech audiometry, and immittance measures for tympanometry and acoustic reflexes. In general, results of peripheral hearing tests show normal hearing acuity in children who have central auditory processing disorders.

A normal foundation of language knowledge is necessary for accurate CAP assessment. Some of the tests rely on neurological responses, but many require responses that incorporate language concepts, such as which word was heard *first*, *left* vs. *right*, etc. It is also important to have basic language awareness of the symbol system and sounds of the language in some of the tests. A significant delay in general language acquisition should not be interpreted as a central auditory processing deficit, even though the child will probably fail most of the CAP tests.

Intellectual functioning should be in a relatively normal or functional age range. Again, directions can be somewhat complex on some tasks. Also, a brain that is already significantly impaired may perform poorly on CAP tasks, but that doesn't necessarily imply that the CANS system is at fault. The child should have a minimal I.Q. level of approximately five years of age.

Exceptions can be made to these parameters, but only by a skilled audiologist with extensive experience in interpreting CAP results. Remember that in children, CAP assessment is evaluating a developing auditory neurological system in which normal myelinization can take up to seven years. It is important to insure a normal neurological foundation before implying deficits. CAP tests were used primarily to assess adults with suspected lesions in the CANS. The evaluation tools are now used to assess the functional integrity of CANS in children, but they must be interpreted carefully. A test result that suggests a significant lesion in an adult could be a normal developmental result in a child. For this reason, it is also important that CAP assessment instruments be normed on children to account for developmental results versus the fully-developed CANS of an adult.

Types of Audiological CAP Assessment Procedures

The usual presentation of auditory stimuli in the everyday world is diotic, i.e., two ears, same signal. In other words, the normal person has two ears that hear the same acoustic signal at the same time. Audiometric tests attempt to alter the typical diotic condition to see how the auditory system responds when the usual signal reception mode is changed. Again, the premise of CAP testing is to stress the system by compromising the signal.

Audiological assessment procedures can be categorized into four main classifications: monotic, dichotic, binaural, and electrophysiological. There are variations within each of these classifications. This section is not intended to teach the various types of audiology options in assessment procedures, but to illustrate assessment options in the various categories. Typical results to be expected in children who are positive for CAPD are also summarized in each assessment procedure section. In general, the test results are used to help determine if the deficit is occurring in the brainstem or the temporal lobe within the CANS system.

• Monotic Tests

In monotic tests, an acoustic stimulus is presented to one ear at a time, i.e., one signal to one ear. Types of monotic tests include the following:

Filtered Speech	Certain frequencies are filtered out or eliminated.
Compressed Speech	The rate of speech is accelerated.
Pitch Pattern Recognition	Changes in pitch/frequency are identified.
Ipsilateral Competing Signals	Speech signals are presented in competition with noise or other speech signals.

Monotic Test Impressions: Monotic listening tasks or ipsilateral competing messages appear to be very sensitive to identifying the presence of central auditory processing disorders at the brainstem level. Audiologists look for a significant discrepancy or assymetry between the scores on the two ears to determine the likelihood of CAPD.

• Dichotic Tests

Dichotic tests use two ears, but they present simultaneous different signals, i.e., two ears, different signals. Dichotic tests are considered by some to be the crux of central auditory processing testing. They are the most definitive for functionally evaluating the competing ipsilateral versus contralateral pathways in the central auditory nervous system. Types of dichotic tests include those listed on the following page.

Competing Digits	Different pairs of numbers are presented simultaneously.
Competing Consonant-Vowels	Different consonant-vowel pairs are presented simultaneously.
Competing Words	Monosyllabic or bisyllabic words are presented simultaneously, such as staggered spondaic words.
Competing Sentences	Different sentences are presented simultaneously.
Contralateral Competing Messages	Nonsense or real sentences are presented against conversational speech that is presented simultaneously.

Dichotic Test Impressions: In general, more difficulty with an ipsilateral competing auditory message suggests central auditory processing or brainstem level difficulty; more difficulty with a contralateral competing auditory message suggests a temporal lobe deficit. Audiologists look for significant ear differences to determine if central auditory processing appears to be a problem. Memory and linguistic variables must be considered in interpretation as the competing messages increase in complexity.

- **Binaural Interaction Tests**

Binaural interaction tests evaluate the listener's ability to sequence or add signals together that are separated and presented alternatively to two ears. For example, a word might be acoustically separated by presenting the first phoneme to the left ear, the second phoneme to the right ear, the third phoneme to the left ear, etc. The listener must cumulatively add the pieces together that are received in the two ears. Examples of binaural tests include the following:

Binaural Fusion	High- and low-frequency components of the same word are separated and presented simultaneously, i.e., the low-frequency components are presented to the left ear and the high-frequency components are presented to the right ear at the same time.
Binaural Separation	The listener attends to information presented to one ear while suppressing information presented simultaneously to the other ear.

Rapidly Alternating Speech	A continuous, sequential signal is presented in quick, alternating bursts between the two ears.
Masking Level Differences	The listener compares speech and noise signals being presented in and out of phase.

Binaural Test Impressions: Children with CAPD demonstrate significantly low scores on binaural tasks when compared to expectations for normal performance. Poor establishment of a dominant ear is also evidenced.

• Electrophysiological Tests

Electrophysiological tests utilize neurological reflex responses and do not require the listener to actually respond. These tests are similar to immittance tests, only they are more sophisticated and evaluate the brainstem level rather than peripheral auditory system. Electrodes are attached to the individual, allowing objective measurement of physiological responses to auditory stimulation. Examples of electrophysiological tests include the following:

Aural Reflex Test	This test measures ipsilateral vs. contralateral reflexes in the stapedial muscle in response to tones.
Auditory Brainstem Response (ABR)	This test measures the evoked response of the early CANS (brainstem).
Cortical Evoked Response	This test measures the evoked response of the later CANS (cortical area).

Electrophysiological Test Impressions: Electrophysiological assessment looks at response latency as measured by wave peaks following the presentation of a sound. In general, children with CAPD show "poorly formed ABR waveforms with substantially delayed peak latencies or an absence of expected peak responses" (Jerger in Keith, 1982). In other words, brainstem level responses are deviant in children with CAP disorders, while temporal lobe language processing disorders evidence normal ABR assessment results.

The assessment situations and general results included in this section are not intended to be definitive, but rather illustrative. A certified audiologist would need to carefully read and examine assessment information for administration and interpretation of the procedures outlined previously before engaging in diagnostic tasks. There are numerous resources to assist professionals in providing more detailed information on the material, as well as practicing audiologists to help define clinical parameters.

CAP Assessment Cautions

CAP testing makes no attempt to evaluate "real life" auditory conditions. The tasks are not functional and are not intended to be. The assessment instruments for CAP are intended to evaluate neurological integrity in a discrete, controlled manner, limiting extraneous variables that could influence results. Applied deficits, such as reading difficulty or language deficits, should never be diagnosed solely through CAP assessment. Linguistic aspects of auditory signal coding and decoding must be administered and interpreted in conjunction with the CAP evaluation results.

Audiologists are urged to interpret CAP assessment results carefully for children six years of age and younger. Results can be influenced by language comprehension issues rather than actual central auditory processing deficits. Maturation effects can be very misleading if experience assessing young children and their resulting performance is not part of one's regular clinical practice.

For these reasons, audiological assessment for central auditory processing needs to carefully minimize linguistic aspects of evaluation tasks to accurately infer central auditory nervous system function. Factors that can significantly influence performance on CAP assessment and falsely suggest CAP deficits rather than language processing deficits are listed in the box below.

Additional Factors That Can Influence CAP Assessment

Inclusion of language comprehension items

Use of linguistically meaningful versus non-meaningful auditory stimuli

Tasks that require linguistic manipulation of an auditory signal

A response mode that requires decoding or linguistic processing rather than simple imitation

Poor attention or focus for auditory stimuli

CAP Assessment Battery

The Central Auditory Nervous System (CANS) is a complex system with incredible internal redundancy. To evaluate the integrity of the system, audiologists stress the system by reducing the redundancy to find out the level of neurological breakdown. To accurately interpret assessment results for central auditory processing, aspects of memory, attention, cognition, and language must be carefully controlled and minimized.

CAP assessment is designed to evaluate the neurological integrity of the auditory system from above the eighth auditory nerve to the cortex level of Heschl's gyrus. If the system has a deficit, the neurological glitch should be demonstrated consistently. In other words, the system will not dysfunction on only one task; the deficit should be demonstrated repeatedly on a series of evaluation tasks that tap into performance of transferring an acoustic signal through the brainstem to the cortex. Deficits in CAP should never be diagnosed from one subtest or task performance. Audiologists look for a pattern or consistency in results on a series of tasks that assess neurological functioning in the CANS.

For this reason, assessment for central auditory processing deficits is generally conducted using a battery of tests to substantiate performance integrity of the CANS. It would be naïve and misleading to believe that central auditory processing deficits could be diagnosed using one test or procedures outlined previously. In reality, multiple tests from the four categories outlined earlier in this chapter (monotic, dichotic, binaural interaction, and electrophysiological tests) are usually conducted to evaluate CAPD. This precaution helps to increase confidence and accuracy when the audiologist interprets assessment results.

Unfortunately, much of the past research correlating CAP assessment results with specific instruments was conducted when language processing variables were not minimized or separated from central auditory processing results. It is important to consult with audiologists who specialize in assessing central auditory processing skills in children to determine specific tests to constitute an appropriate battery. Assessment procedures continue to be refined with increased reliability and validity for evaluating children's developing audiological systems.

A sample battery is included to illustrate the scope of an assessment battery for CAPD. Variations in the assessment procedures discussed previously are apparent in this outline. The sequence helps to show the diversity of auditory tasks typically included in CAP assessment. It also helps to indicate the time allotment and extensiveness of testing procedures, which can be an unrealistic expectation for many children.

Dr. Jeanane Ferre, an audiologist in private practice in the Chicago area who specializes in central auditory processing disorders, advocates that a CAP battery include the following components:

- Standard audiometric and immittance tests
- Monaural low-redundancy tasks
- Binaural interaction tasks
- Binaural integration tasks
- Binaural separation tasks
- Temporal patterning tasks

Functional Auditory Skills Assessment

Some auditory skills have typically been classified as *non-audiological assessment areas* of central auditory processing. In fact, they involve auditory tasks at a rudimentary processing level designated at Heschl's gyrus in the neurological model. The auditory abilities included here have been jointly evaluated by audiologists and speech-language pathologists, but they probably best fit under the area of speech-language pathology because the acoustic signal has entered the cortex, and beginning levels of linguistic knowledge must be applied to the signal in order to interpret it correctly.

The auditory skills outlined in this section are the building blocks for language processing tasks of increased linguistic and cognitive complexity. The ability to perform these auditory tasks has direct bearing on language and learning. They function as the foundation for reading, spelling, verbal and written language, and other more integrated language tasks.

Many of these skills have multiple identifying titles or names. Early information on processing labeled these tasks as "Auditory _____," based on the model of processing being performed on auditory information. One of the first assessment models originated at the University of Illinois in the 1960s from what was called a psycholinguistic model of learning. Based on Osgood's principles (1957), Kirk (1968) developed the *Illinois Test of Psycholinguistic Abilities*, better known as the *ITPA*. The test was designed to evaluate discrete essential components of the communication processes of transferring, receiving, and interpreting messages between two people. The twelve subtests of the original *ITPA* are listed in the box at the top of the following page.

The psychometric properties of the *ITPA* were questioned in the literature (Burns & Watson, 1973; Rykman & Wiegerink, 1969; Wiig & Semel, 1980; Bloom & Lahey, 1978; Wing, 1982). Despite the criticism, the *ITPA* was one of the first tests to attempt to discriminate a hierarchy of discrete

```
+-----------------------------------------------------------------+
|                                                                 |
|                    Subtests of the *ITPA*                       |
|                                                                 |
|   Auditory Reception          Grammatic Closure                 |
|                                                                 |
|   Visual Reception            Auditory Closure                  |
|                                                                 |
|   Auditory Association        Visual Closure                    |
|                                                                 |
|   Visual Association          Auditory Sequential Memory         |
|                                                                 |
|   Verbal Expression           Visual Sequential Memory          |
|                                                                 |
|   Manual Expression           Sound Blending                    |
|                                                                 |
+-----------------------------------------------------------------+
```

language skills that contributed to processing. In 1978, Willeford and Billger (in Katz, 1978) referred to the *ITPA* as a bible for many speech clinicians because it was used so extensively, either by itself or in combination with other assessment instruments.

As central auditory processing and language processing began to be more differentiated, the language area of phonology began to overshadow the generic use of *auditory* to identify these types of skills. Labels changed to *phonemic* rather than *auditory* as functional auditory skills were identified by titles of *phonemic segmentation, phonemic synthesis,* etc. Since the 1990s, *phonemic awareness* has emerged as a core skill for language processing and seems to have replaced some, but not all, of the earlier identified auditory tasks.

The *ITPA* was revised and updated in 2001, consistent with the new emphasis on phonological and linguistic aspects of communication. The *Illinois Test of Psycholinguistic Abilities-3* (Hammill, Mather, & Roberts, 2001) reflects increased focus on spoken and written communication by assessing reading and spelling responses to presented auditory stimuli. The twelve subtests in the *ITPA-3* are listed in the following box.

```
+-----------------------------------------------------------------+
|                                                                 |
|                    Subtests of the *ITPA-3*                     |
|                                                                 |
|   Spoken Analogies            Sentence Sequencing               |
|                                                                 |
|   Spoken Vocabulary           Written Vocabulary                |
|                                                                 |
|   Morphological Closure       Sight Decoding                    |
|                                                                 |
|   Syntactic Sentences         Sound Decoding                    |
|                                                                 |
|   Sound Deletion              Sight Spelling                    |
|                                                                 |
|   Rhyming Sequences           Sound Spelling                    |
|                                                                 |
+-----------------------------------------------------------------+
```

Despite the modification in labels, the auditory skills encompassed continue to gain attention in the fields of communication disorders and learning. A child's ability to discriminate the acoustic features of sounds contributes significantly to developing more complex, integrated language skills for academic success.

Purpose of Functional Auditory Skills Assessment

There are two primary reasons to evaluate functional auditory skills. The first is to determine if auditory information has been transferred through the brainstem to the cortex intactly. Second, if the auditory information enters the cortex accurately, how well can the individual discern specific features of the acoustic information?

On the neurological model for processing, this area of assessment is Brodmann numbers 41 and 42. The structure is Heschl's gyrus, and in Luria's model, it constitutes the primary zone of the temporal lobe, second function unit. This is the overlap area where auditory processing and beginning levels of language processing occur.

If Heschl's gyrus does not function adequately, then higher-level language processing will be jeopardized. It is important to evaluate the integrity of the auditory signal before trying to assess if difficulties exist in more complex language processing abilities.

Prerequisites for Functional Auditory Skills Assessment

The same prerequisites as those outlined for CAP testing apply to accurate assessment of functional auditory skills. Hearing acuity should be within normal limits, intelligence should be in a functional range, and language comprehension needs to approximate a four- to five-year-old's level to understand basic instructions in tasks.

It is important to insure that evaluation of functional auditory skills is fairly discrete and controlled. Other variables can significantly influence assessment results and mislead the professional in programming intervention. One example is the way auditory discrimination tests were used in the past. Two pictures were presented, such as *rake* and *lake*. Then the child heard the two words pronounced and was asked if the words were the same or different. Children who answered in error were presumed to have difficulty hearing the difference between phonemes. In reality, variables such as concept confusion (*same* vs. *different*), word retrieval, visual picture recognition, and other variables influenced the results.

Types of Functional Auditory Skills

Most of the tests to assess functional auditory skills consist of taped presentation of the auditory stimuli and a scoresheet for recording a child's responses. Some tests rely on the clinician to present the auditory stimuli in a clear verbal manner. The subtest titles are not always an accurate reflection of the skill being assessed as outlined in the neurological model. The professional choosing assessment instruments must carefully evaluate what is being presented and asked of the child in terms of a response.

The primary skills included in functional auditory assessment at the level of Heschl's gyrus are listed and defined in the following section. Again, variations might exist in specific assessment instrument titles and descriptions. Also remember that many of these tasks are now evaluated under titles of *phonemic awareness* rather than generic *auditory skills*.

Auditory Analysis	breaking a word into specific sound segments
Auditory Association	pairing a sound with its source
Auditory Attention	being aware of and attending to auditory signals
Auditory Blending/Synthesis	forming a word by blending individual phonemes together
Auditory Closure	filling in missing or distorted acoustic information to complete a word or message
Auditory Discrimination	distinguishing similarities and differences between sounds
Auditory Figure Ground	attending to relevant linguistic information presented with background competing auditory stimuli of noise or linguistic information
Auditory Localization	ability to determine the location of a sound source
Auditory Memory	retaining components of an auditory signal over a period of time
Auditory Sequencing	remembering auditory information in a specific order (subset of auditory memory)

82

Significant difficulty with any of these skills indicates a processing breakdown in the earliest levels of linguistic coding on the acoustic signal. These skills should be remediated before moving on to more complex language processing tasks.

Functional Auditory Skills Assessment Cautions

The primary purpose of evaluation at the primary zone level is to determine if the acoustic signal is being received accurately in the cortex for language processing. Most of the time, processing disorders occur at the level of the cortex in primary, secondary, or tertiary zones of the second functional unit. The incredible redundancy of the CANS insures fairly accurate reception of auditory stimuli in the primary zone.

If consistently poor performance is evidenced on several functional auditory assessment tasks, referral should be made to an audiologist for CAP assessment. It is important to determine where and when the auditory signal becomes compromised, if possible. This information will have an influence on the type of remediation suggestions. However, as mentioned previously, CAP assessment involves some fairly complex directions and focused listening. Some children have not attained a developmental level conducive to accuracy in CAP test results. It is often easier to assume integrity of the CANS system and begin assessment at the functional auditory skills level, rather than routinely beginning the assessment procedures for processing at the level of an audiologist.

Most of the time, poor performance in the primary zone should result in a referral to an audiologist for CAP assessment. Integrity of the central auditory nervous system should be evaluated if a child is not able to determine acoustic aspects of the signal. Once CAP deficits have been ruled out, intervention can work on building improved phonemic awareness and functional auditory skills.

The majority of processing deficits are language processing rather than central auditory processing. Applying linguistic knowledge to acoustic stimuli received is the usual problem in the majority of processing disorders. Remediation needs to begin by improving phonemic and acoustic awareness, then scaffold into language knowledge in semantics, syntax, and pragmatics.

Sample Tests to Evaluate Functional Auditory Skills

There are a variety of assessment instruments to evaluate the primary zone. These instruments vary significantly in administration time, type of output response, standardization, result interpretation, and discreteness of task design. The clinician choosing the assessment tools should carefully evaluate the results and interpret performance consistent with the neurological model. Some tests make large leaps from discrete skill assessment to suggested interpretation of results having global impact on language and learning. Others state that they are designed to assess functional auditory skills, but actually involve higher-level language processing skills. Clinicians must analyze test tasks to determine what processing skills are actually being evaluated.

In *Auditory Processes* (1993), Pamela Gillet explores several of the functional auditory skills defined above and lists assessment instruments for each area. Her lists are extensive, but they overlap with language processing skills in several areas. There are additional resources available listing possible assessment tools in the area of functional auditory processing. I have listed some of the better known instruments I prefer to assess the functional auditory skills and provided rationale to explain my perceptions.

- *Illinois Test of Psycholinguistic Abilities (ITPA)*
  Auditory Closure
  Auditory Blending
  Auditory Sequential Memory

  These three subtests of the original *ITPA* provide a quick look at integrity for phonemic awareness and memory to retain auditory elements long enough to attach meaning to them. Even though the norms have been questioned, the age equivalency charts provide a rough estimate for comparison to peers. The results can assist speech-language pathologists in determining if questions should be raised regarding central auditory processing skills or if the problem probably exists at the level of language processing.

- *Illinois Test of Psycholinguistic Abilities-3 (ITPA-3)*
  Sound Deletion
  Rhyming Sequences
  Sound Decoding

  These three subtests of the *ITPA-3* examine phonology, phonemic awareness, and phonemic sequential memory within a reading and spelling academic context. While more emphasis is on sound-symbol decoding than pure auditory skills, these subtests can provide information regarding a child's development of the auditory foundation for processing.

- ## *Goldman-Fristoe-Woodcock Auditory Series*
  Auditory Discrimination
  Auditory Figure Ground
  Auditory Memory
  Auditory Selective Attention

  The *Goldman-Fristoe-Woodcock Auditory Series* (Goldman, Fristoe, & Woodcock, 1974) provides an audio cassette tape presentation of test stimuli. The child listens and responds while the clinician records answers. The subtests are rather lengthy, and the voice presentation is very monotone, but the instruments do provide good information on functional aptitude in the auditory areas designated. There are other tests in the series, including Sound-Symbol Correspondence, which can be helpful when children have reading problems.

- ## *Screening Test for Auditory Processing Disorders (SCAN)*

  Dr. Robert Keith, audiologist, designed a test that can be administered by speech-language pathologists to screen the CANS. While somewhat of a challenge to score for non-audiologists the first few times, this screening includes dichotic tests that can improve a speech-language pathologist's understanding of central auditory processing tasks. The directions can be challenging for young children, and they require headphones to deliver competing messages to the ears. If questions regarding the central auditory processing system are present, it is a nice alternative before referral for full CAP testing. It also gives an idea to the parents and speech-language pathologist as to whether the child is capable of handling the CAP assessment tasks. Significant difficulty with the test should not result in diagnosis of CAP; it should prompt referral for further assessment.

- ## Assessing Children's Language Comprehension (ACLC)

  This older test is excellent for assessing auditory memory. It checks comprehension to insure adequate vocabulary before evaluating functional application of auditory information. The test begins with one critical unit, and then assesses two, three, and four critical units. Picture foils are provided to help the clinician determine if a pattern exists in the way a child responds who evidenced poor auditory attention. The foils help determine if the first, second, third, or fourth element is usually missed. Norms are not available, but the test provides valuable functional information about auditory memory skills.

- ***Phonemic Awareness Test (PAT)***

  This test is one of several that have been developed consistent with the phonological foundation to build higher-level language processing skills. Rather than title the functional tasks under a general *auditory* heading, the test uses phonemes as the unit of acoustic information and manipulates them in a large variety of tasks. The test is often used to help diagnose foundation skills for reading, spelling, and other academic tasks.

  Not all of the functional auditory skills listed have to be assessed, but a variety should be sampled to determine if acoustic signals are being discriminated and manipulated adequately to integrate more complex levels of language coding.

Language Processing Assessment

The central auditory processing assessment model followed an acoustic stimulus through the central auditory nervous system. That progression identified a neurological hierarchy for maturational development, as well as auditory processing ability. The assessment tasks were discrete and attempted to isolate neurological movement and interpretation of the auditory signal.

The objective auditory model outlined in the processing continuum has been lacking in language processing assessment approaches. Tests were designed that included a variety of tasks, most consisting of multiple language variables in each subtest activity. Based on performance results, goals were written to address any language areas in deficit. A hierarchy or continuum of language processing was not applied. Therapy was hit and miss, targeting skills assessed as *weak*, with no corresponding neurological model to guide neurological maturation or developmental order of language processing skills.

Extending the neuropsychological model of the processing continuum provided a developmental model for language processing. The behavioral approach of simply writing goals to address any areas of deficit, regardless of language developmental levels, was replaced by a more orderly evaluation of language maturation in a neurological progression of processing. Meaning is attached in the secondary zone, and then higher levels of thought are accomplished through integration of language information in the tertiary zone. Processing then moves to the third functional unit for organization and output. A beginning, middle, and ending point could finally be applied to language processing skills, rather than guesstimating what language goal should be addressed next.

Language processing assessment must be guided by and consistent with the neuropsychological Processing Continuum Model. Language processing begins at a rudimentary level in the primary zone, but is concentrated in the secondary zone. Once the integrity of the secondary zone processing has been evaluated, then language processing assessment moves to tertiary zone skills.

It is also important that tasks be as discrete as possible. Other language variables should be carefully controlled and minimized so as not to affect performance. For example, to assess the secondary zone of the temporal lobe, only auditory input should be provided. Many tests use picture stimuli, involving the occipital lobe primary, secondary, and tertiary zones to assist in the language processing task. A task using visual stimuli to assess the auditory secondary zone can lead to erroneous diagnosis.

Sample Language Processing Hierarchy

Language abilities develop in a hierarchy of increased cognitive complexity, following the neurological model. Language processing begins in the secondary zone, where meaning is attached to an acoustic stimulus. An example of a language processing hierarchy is listed below.

- Nouns—labels
- Verbs—functions
- Situational Association
- Categorization
- Similarity
- Difference
- Multiple Meaning

There is nothing magic about the language tasks outlined here except that they are arranged in a hierarchy of development. For example, the first class of words an infant acquires is usually nouns to label pertinent objects in his world. Once he has names for objects, he attaches functional meaning to those labels, defining what each object does or what he does with it. For verb terms to have functional meaning, they must be attached to an object. Once the child understands an identifying object label and what it does, he begins to associate it with other objects usually experienced in the same situation. The child can't associate by situation if he doesn't know what the objects and their functions are. Gradually the association by a concrete situation leads to categorization skills of grouping by similarity. Again, the other language levels are prerequisite to categorization. A child can't group if he doesn't know what they are, what they do, or when they are used. Those language features must be acquired before categorization skills can develop. Items are grouped or categorized by similar features. Once the grouping is realized, a child begins to differentiate the distinguishing features that separate items within the category. Language skills of similarity and difference won't develop until the processing hierarchy has established the prerequisite levels of knowledge.

A speech-language pathologist could design an alternative hierarchy of language processing, utilizing different discrete language tasks. The important aspect is the hierarchy of increased meaning attached to basic vocabulary items acquired by the child. There is no way to jump right to a categorization level of language processing without first acquiring earlier levels of meaning.

Language processing generally focuses on the hierarchy of semantic complexity, but an argument could be made for a processing hierarchy in acquiring syntax, phonology, and pragmatic areas of language. Language acquisition follows a pattern or progression of increased linguistic complexity, building gradually on previous language knowledge to attain new levels of meaning.

It is important to assess language processing in a hierarchy of increased linguistic complexity. With careful evaluation, intervention can be very focused and effective in programming remedial services at the earliest level of deficit rather than haphazardly choosing language tasks to address.

Purpose of Language Processing Assessment

Language processing is the ability to attach linguistic meaning of increased complexity to auditory information received and then formulate a response. A "pure" language processing problem cannot be attributed to other major disorders, such as mental retardation, emotional disabilities, motor-based speech production problems, organic damage, or specific language impairments in the acquisition of semantics, syntax, phonology, or pragmatics. The population at risk for language processing disorders demonstrates normal intellectual potential and is approximately age-commensurate in language acquisition measurements. A language processing problem is difficulty in accessing language ability already acquired and efficiently integrating those basic foundation language skills to formulate more complex thoughts and responses. Indications of a language processing disorder can be subtle and often exist as a component or subtype of learning disabilities and other language impairments.

88

Language processing assessment should isolate discrete language skills, evaluating secondary zone temporal lobe association abilities, and then progressing to tertiary zone integration language skills. A neurological hierarchy should be utilized to impose a more objective approach to language processing assessment.

Prerequisites for Language Processing Assessment

Three requirements must be met in order to accurately interpret performance deficits as a language processing disorder:

1. The acoustic signal has been received intactly in the cortex (primary zone assessment).

2. The child has normal/near-normal acquisition of basic receptive/expressive language skills.

3. The child has normal/near-normal intellectual functioning.

Language processing presumes that auditory information has been received accurately in the primary zone of the temporal lobe. The deficit occurs as the child attempts to attach meaning in an increased hierarchy of linguistic difficulty. If the signal has been distorted or compromised before it reaches the secondary zone for language processing, the impaired stimulus may be creating the difficulty in adequately attaching meaning.

The processing continuum assumes that the individual has acquired the prerequisite linguistic knowledge to attach meaning to the auditory signal. Basic vocabulary knowledge should be approximately age commensurate as measured on a receptive vocabulary test, such as the *Peabody Picture Vocabulary Test-Revised* (PPVT) or the *Receptive One Word Picture Vocabulary Test* (ROWPVT). A child must have developed a lexicon of nouns or a basic object vocabulary to attach increased levels of meaning to the term. If the child's basic vocabulary is in deficit, then a language *acquisition* problem exists, not a language processing problem. Language processing occurs on top of or in addition to basic language acquisition.

When cognitive development is impaired, the level of language processing should be commensurate with the mental or functioning age of the child. It is not accurate to say that a child who is chronologically ten years old with a mental age of five should be processing language at a level equal to ten years. The general language functioning age is the level of expectation for processing ability. It is not possible to exceed the language developmental age since processing is conducted on the linguistic developmental knowledge.

The importance of these prerequisites will be applied in some of the case examples at the end of this chapter. These three aspects are the variables a speech-pathologist needs to differentiate between a developmental language problem and a language processing problem.

Types of Language Processing Assessment Procedures

Assessment of language processing abilities should consider the variables listed below when choosing evaluation instruments.

Language Processing Assessments

Input limited to auditory stimuli.

Evaluate language complexity in subtest tasks.

Include discrete, isolated language tasks.

Increase processing demand to include complex language tasks.

Progress to multimodality input to assess integrated language tasks.

Secondary zone temporal lobe assessment is the first area that must be evaluated in language processing. To maintain a discrete focus in the temporal lobe function, input should be limited to auditory stimuli. It is also important to evaluate the language processing demand or complexity in subtest tasks. Most tests do not order the subtests in any hierarchy of language complexity. It is up to the speech-language pathologists to decide easiest-to-hardest language demand. Variables should be controlled so that only one specific language processing skill is being evaluated. Then the clinician can gradually progress into more complex, integrated language tasks.

For example, consider a language subtest that gives directions to manipulate different colored shapes into various positions. The child performs poorly and a language processing disorder is diagnosed. What language processing area is in deficit that should be addressed through goals? Did the child do poorly because of poor spatial concept knowledge, lack of color knowledge, shape knowledge, or poor auditory memory? The clinician doesn't know without extensive follow-up assessment to discriminate among the multiple variables that weren't controlled in the task. This example illustrates a poor use of language processing assessment time. Evaluation did nothing to help the clinician pinpoint the beginning level of language processing deficits.

That isn't to say that assessment using other sensory modalities must be avoided. Valuable information can be gained by knowing that if visual information is supplemented, language processing skills improve. This is important information to know when designing intervention.

Language Processing Assessment Cautions

Language processing performance can be influenced by other factors during assessment procedures. Not minimizing these other variables can enhance or hinder language processing results, leading to false assumptions about performance.

When assessment instruments to evaluate language processing use picture stimuli, more of the cortex has been energized to participate in the task. Both the primary zones of the occipital and temporal lobes are receiving stimuli, which turns on the secondary zones of both occipital and temporal lobes and energizes the tertiary zone. The child may do well on the task, leading the speech-language pathologist to presume that language processing is not the deficit. However, the task did not isolate the secondary zone temporal lobe to determine how it functions. The area was not discretely evaluated, yet interpretation falsely believed the area to function adequately.

The opposite can also occur. A child was evaluated using a subtest for following directions by pointing to shapes in various positions. The child never pointed accurately and failed the test miserably. The interpretation was a language processing deficit, based on the subtest performance. However, upon returning the child to the classroom, the teacher asked why he didn't have his glasses with him! Visual acuity problems (occipital lobe) led to a false diagnosis of language processing (temporal lobe) problems.

It is critical that language processing assessment isolate language performance as much as possible to the appropriate mediating area in the brain. That means that secondary zone assessment for language processing is auditory input only. Tertiary zone assessment can involve integration of the other modalities.

Adjunct Areas of Language Processing Assessment

Two adjunct skills can have a significant impact on language processing assessment results: auditory memory and word retrieval. It is important to evaluate these two areas separately to determine their influence on language processing assessment results.

• Auditory Memory

Poor memory can impact language processing by compromising the child's ability to retain information long enough to attach meaning to it. The typical expectation for short-term working memory is seven-to-ten items. That's why phone numbers and ZIP codes try not to exceed seven digits—people can't remember them! Seven-to-ten items is the usual limit for non-related memory. Related memory is longer because context allows us to retain more units by attaching meaning.

Assessment of short term memory can be conducted using the Auditory Sequential Memory subtest of the original *Illinois Test of Psycholinguistic Abilities* (Kirk, McCarthy, & Kirk, 1968). The test uses numerals, beginning with two in a sequence and working up to ten.

Related memory can be assessed using any syntactic screening tests where a sentence is read and the child must repeat it back. The morphological length of sentences repeated back by the child will estimate auditory memory for related information.

• Word Retrieval

Word retrieval involves two aspects of language ability—efficiency and accuracy. The ability to retrieve acquired language knowledge should be relatively quick (efficient) and correct (accurate). If efficiency is a problem, a latency will be shown by a lag time between questions and answers. The normal question-response latency is two-to-four seconds. Longer than that implies some difficulty in efficiency aspects of retrieval. Accuracy problems will be noted by pulling terms that might be close or related in some way (e.g., phonologically similar, semantically similar) but the wrong term. The child might also never find the word and give up or say "I don't know."

Word retrieval problems are one of the cardinal features of language processing disorders. Most of the children with language processing disorders struggle to retrieve learned information accurately and efficiently. The important concept to remember is that with word retrieval problems, the language has been acquired and is in the child's lexicon, but the child can't access it.

Assessment for word retrieval can be addressed formally or informally. One of the most well-designed assessment instruments to evaluate this area is *The Test of Word Finding* (German, 1986). An easy informal method is the *Northwestern Word Latency Test.* Three timed trials for picture naming are presented to determine if the child's retrieval time becomes faster and words retrieved stay the same or change. Word retrieval can also be informally evaluated by observing accuracy and latency on other language processing measurements.

Language Processing Assessment Battery

A variety of evaluation instruments can be used to assess language processing. However, unlike the central auditory processing tests, the speech-language pathologist must impose the neuropsychological model into the tests chosen. Very few were designed within that theoretical framework.

The typical language processing assessment should cover primary, secondary, and tertiary zone language tasks. Word retrieval and auditory memory should also be included to evaluate their impact on language processing test performance. Sample assessment instruments that have been used for processing are discussed next, with my clinical impressions to guide you in their use for evaluating language processing.

- ### ITPA Subtests: Auditory Sequential Memory, Auditory Closure, and Auditory Blending

  These three subtests from the original *ITPA* require minimal time but provide insight on primary zone function (Auditory Closure and Blending) and the adjunct area of memory. If the child struggles with the first two tasks, a referral for central auditory processing assessment might be beneficial. Another option would be to conduct testing in more of the functional auditory skill areas (e.g., *SCAN*) to see if consistently poor performance is evidenced in primary zone skills. If memory indicates a short-term retention of fewer than five items, language processing tasks with complex directions must be interpreted carefully so as not to imply a language deficit when memory could have impacted the ability to attach meaning.

- ### *Peabody Picture Vocabulary Test—Revised (PPVT)*

  Basic receptive vocabulary acquisition age must be determined to accurately interpret language processing scores. A child cannot be expected to process language at a higher level of complexity than the child's lexicon development. The *Peabody Picture Vocabulary Test- 3rd Edition* (Dunn & Dunn, 1997) evaluates more diverse language development (e.g., nouns, verbs, adjectives, categories, etc.) as compared to some other vocabulary tests that consist primarily of nouns.

• Language Processing Test (LPT)

The *Language Processing Test-Revised (*Richard & Hanner, 1995) is the only test designed using the theoretical construct of Luria's neuropsychological model of a processing continuum. Subtests are arranged in a hierarchy of language complexity, allowing the clinician to interpret the level of processing breakdown from results. The test moves through the secondary zone temporal lobe, using discrete language skills of increasingly complex linguistic knowledge. The instrument evaluates pre-school beginning levels of language processing (i.e., pretests) through elementary school age.

• The Word Test—Revised

The Word Test—Revised (Huisingh, Barrett, Bowers, LoGiudice, & Orman, 1990) assesses higher-level language processing abilities than are targeted on the *LPT*. The confusion lies in some subtest areas carrying the same name, but demanding very different levels of language complexity in the task. For example, the Association subtest on the *LPT* is a low- level concrete task of noun association within context. The Association subtest on *The WORD Test* presents four terms (memory) and asks the child which one doesn't belong (categorization) and why (similarity and difference). Several discrete skills from the *LPT* are required in this one task. There is not an inconsistency in performance for a child who passes Association on *LPT* and fails Association on *The WORD Test*. The inconsistency is in task design and interpretation. All of the subtests on *The WORD Test* are relatively high-level secondary zone temporal lobe tasks. If a child does well on *LPT* but language processing is still suspected as the problem, *The WORD Test* often picks up the problem. It is important to remember that the subtests are not in any order of language demand.

• The Test of Problem Solving (TOPS)—Revised

The Test of Problem Solving—Revised (Bowers, Barrett, Huisingh, Orman, & LoGiudice, 1994) targets the tertiary zone in the language processing hierarchy. Pictures are presented to represent a situational context for the child. However, the answers are not concretely available; the child must extrapolate language knowledge and experiences to formulate an appropriate response. Without basic discrete language processing abilities from the secondary zone, a child is likely to struggle with *The Test of Problem Solving—Revised.*

• The Listening Test

The *Listening Test* (Barrett, Huisingh, Bowers, LoGiudice, & Orman, 1992) is a very useful assessment instrument for evaluating more complex levels of language processing. The test content is higher level than the *LPT*, but primarily secondary zone due to auditory input only. The questions tap integrated language problem solving, reasoning, and comprehension of information presented auditorially.

• The Clinical Evaluation of Language Fundamentals—3rd Edition (CELF)

The *Clinical Evaluation of Language Fundamentals—3rd Edition* (Semel, Wiig, & Secord, 1995) has been used widely by speech-language pathologists to diagnose language processing deficits. The tasks on the *CELF* are very complex and primarily tertiary zone skills. Variables are not always well controlled, so tasks are not discrete, and often follow-up probing or assessment is necessary to sort out poor performance. Subtests are not in any order of difficulty, so the clinician must impose a hierarchy based on personal assessment of tasks. The complexity of tasks makes diagnosis and level for beginning intervention a challenge to differentiate.

• The Test of Word Finding (TWF)

The *Test of Word Finding* (German, 1986) provides information in one of the most important adjunct areas of language processing disorders. The *TWF* assesses language comprehension for all items missed. This insures that acquisition or language development is NOT the deficit, but retrieval or access to learned knowledge is the problem. Both accuracy and efficiency are assessed on this well designed and standardized instrument.

Case Examples of Processing Assessment

Several case examples are provided to give speech-language pathologists experience in using assessment results to determine which area(s) of processing appear to be intact and where deficits might lie. The assessment battery meets minimal evaluation requirements, in my opinion. Performance might prompt further assessment to more accurately interpret the results before generating intervention objectives.

The same battery of tests is used for all the case examples, so the variety of instruments does not compound the learning process. It is easier to learn how to "read between the lines" when the evaluation instruments are constant and you can compare across cases. Age range is also controlled to be fairly consistent. In most cases, standardization results are reported rather than raw scores since they are more reliable numbers for interpretation. Subtests from the original *ITPA* are reported due to the auditory-verbal nature of the tasks. The *ITPA-3* relies more on decoding skills in a reading and spelling format. A clinician currently might choose to use subtests from the *Phonemic Awareness Test (PAT)* or *ITPA-3*, but additional variables are introduced (sound-symbol association) that confound impressions for screening the area of central auditory processing.

Each case reports formal assessment results, followed by questions for the clinician to answer. Following the questions is a guideline for interpreting aspects of the language processing disorder—but don't move to the interpretation until you have tried your own skills at diagnostic interpretation. At this point, you are only working to gather general impressions. These cases are expanded upon in remediation sections by providing specific subtest results to help you further explore test interpretation before writing goals.

Here are a few assumptions to keep in mind as you interpret results:

- Assume normal intelligence (unless there are indications otherwise).

- Assume normal hearing acuity (passed a hearing screening test).

- Assume teacher concerns, based on an appropriate score on a completed Behavioral Checklist for Processing Difficulties, page 69.

Remember, it is just as important to know what is intact and working within the processing continuum as it is to know where glitches are. The remediation model advocates using strengths to approach weaknesses; this concept is expanded upon in subsequent chapters. Your intervention will only be as effective as your ability to sort out the source of the processing problem. It's not very efficient to work generically and not target the actual area of deficit.

Have fun playing detective!

Case 1: Tanya

Chronological Age: 8-11

Test Results

ITPA	Raw Score	Age Score	Scaled Score
Auditory Closure	22	7-11	35
Sound Blending	20	8-2	35
Sequential Memory	21	5-8	29

LPT	Age Equivalency	Percentile Rank	Standard Score
	8-11	55	102

TOPS—Revised	Age Equivalency	Percentile Rank	Standard Score
	7-8	15	85

TWF			
Standard Score	By Age: 112	By Grade: 112	
Percentile Rank	By Age: 80	By Grade: 80	
Word Finding Profile: Fast & Accurate			

Interpretation Questions

1. Are there problems/concerns about the primary zone? (Auditory Closure & Sound Blending)

2. Are there problems/concerns about the secondary zone? (*LPT*)

3. Are there problems/concerns about the tertiary zone? (*TOPS—Revised*)

4. Adjunct areas: any memory or word retrieval influence on results?
   (Sequential Memory & *TWF*)

5. Are there other referrals or areas to pursue in further assessment? What areas in the processing hierarchy are probably intact or in deficit?

(See answers on the next page.)

Case 1: Tanya

1. Does not appear to have a primary zone problem; a CAP referral probably is not necessary.

2. Secondary zone (LPT) is age commensurate; no significant problems.

3. Tertiary zone integration tasks are not significantly discrepant; right at one standard deviation from the norm, but weaker than secondary zone.

4. Word retrieval is not a problem.

5. Tanya's problems appear to be in the early stages of a deficit. Memory is weak and may be contributing to deficits; it could be further addressed. While tertiary zone skills are not a significant problem yet, Tanya is not integrating simple language information processed in the secondary zone into more complex tertiary zone language tasks at a commensurate level. Further assessment of complex secondary and tertiary zones may be helpful. It might be beneficial to administer *The WORD Test—Revised* or the *The Listening Test* to further evaluate more complex secondary zone skills. An additional tertiary zone test, such as *TOLD, CELF,* etc., might also be beneficial to further evaluate the integration of Tanya's language skills.

Case 2: Roger

Chronological Age: 9.0

Test Results

ITPA	Raw Score	Age Score	Scaled Score
Auditory Closure	20	6-9	29
Sound Blending	2	2-4	15
Sequential Memory	27	7-7	33

LPT	Age Equivalency	Percentile Rank	Standard Score
	7-9	27	90

TOPS—Revised	Age Equivalency	Percentile Rank	Standard Score
	7-2	6	77

TWF			
	Standard Score	By Age: 112	By Grade: 112
	Percentile Rank	By Age: 80	By Grade: 80
	Word Finding Profile: Fast & Accurate		

Interpretation Questions

1. Are there problems/concerns about the primary zone? (Auditory Closure & Sound Blending)

2. Are there problems/concerns about the secondary zone? (*LPT*)

3. Are there problems/concerns about the tertiary zone? (*TOPS—Revised*)

4. Adjunct areas: any memory or word retrieval influence on results?
   (Sequential Memory & *TWF*)

5. Are there other referrals or areas to pursue in further assessment? What areas in the processing hierarchy are probably intact or in deficit?

(See answers on the next page.)

Case 2: Roger

1. Primary zone is questionable. Test results are incongruent, but a significant problem was apparent in sound blending. CAP referral would probably be beneficial.

2. Secondary zone (LPT) is age commensurate; no significant problems.

3. Tertiary zone integration tasks are below one standard deviation and significantly discrepant from language skills demonstrated on secondary zone language tasks.

4. Word retrieval is not a problem; Memory is within age expectations and does not appear to be a significant factor.

5. Roger may need additional assessment of functional auditory skills. He would be a good candidate for *SCAN* or some additional functional auditory assessments. If his performance is weak, referral to an audiologist for a CAP assessment should be completed. The speech-language pathologist should also further explore tertiary zone language tasks, since more complex integrated language tasks were weaker than discrete focused language performance on the *LPT*.

Case 3: David

Chronological Age: 8.8

Test Results

ITPA	Raw Score	Age Score	Scaled Score
Auditory Closure	19	6-5	29
Sound Blending	23	above norms	38
Sequential Memory	21	5-8	29

LPT	Age Equivalency	Percentile Rank	Standard Score
	7-1	13	84

TOPS—Revised	Age Equivalency	Percentile Rank	Standard Score
	8-0	23	91

TWF			
Standard Score	By Age: 143+	By Grade: 145+	
Percentile Rank	By Age: 99.8	By Grade: 99.9	
Word Finding Profile: Fast & Accurate			

Interpretation Questions

1. Are there problems/concerns about the primary zone? (Auditory Closure & Sound Blending)

2. Are there problems/concerns about the secondary zone? (*LPT*)

3. Are there problems/concerns about the tertiary zone? (*TOPS—Revised*)

4. Adjunct areas: any memory or word retrieval influence on results?
   (Sequential Memory & *TWF*)

5. Are there other referrals or areas to pursue in further assessment? What areas in the processing hierarchy are probably intact or in deficit?

(See answers on the next page.)

Case 3: David

1. The primary zone has one very strong performance and one weak.

2. Secondary zone *LPT* performance is borderline weak, just under one standard deviation from the norm.

3. Tertiary skills are age commensurate.

4. Word retrieval is not a problem; memory is poor.

5. David's memory problems could have contributed to his poor Auditory Closure performance. It is interesting that when only an auditory stimulus is presented, David struggles (secondary zone), but he does better when allowed to use tertiary integration and pick up help from other modalities. This is a good example of language processing problems that occur when academic information is only presented auditorily. The language association zone struggles to attach meaning without visual or other associative information to add contextual cues. Add memory problems and academic difficulties are likely to compound over time unless weaknesses are addressed. Goals should target secondary zone language processing as well as memory. If intervention in language processing is progressing slowly, more in-depth assessment of David's primary zone and central auditory processing could be beneficial.

102

Case 4: Chris

Chronological Age: 8.4

Test Results

ITPA		Raw Score	Age Score	Scaled Score
	Auditory Closure	21	7-3	34
	Sound Blending	22	above norms	38
	Sequential Memory	23	6-3	31

LPT	Age Equivalency	Percentile Rank	Standard Score
	5-5	4	74

TOPS—Revised	Age Equivalency	Percentile Rank	Standard Score
	below norms	2	61

TWF			
	Standard Score	By Age: <73	By Grade: <70
	Percentile Rank	By Age: < 4	By Grade: < 2
	Word Finding Profile: Fast & Inaccurate		

Interpretation Questions

1. Are there problems/concerns about the primary zone? (Auditory Closure & Sound Blending)

2. Are there problems/concerns about the secondary zone? (*LPT*)

3. Are there problems/concerns about the tertiary zone? (*TOPS—Revised*)

4. Adjunct areas: any memory or word retrieval influence on results? (Sequential Memory & *TWF*)

5. Are there other referrals or areas to pursue in further assessment? What areas in the processing hierarchy are probably intact or in deficit?

(See answers on the next page.)

Case 4: Chris

1. The primary zone does not appear to have problems; Chris demonstrated his strongest performance in this area.

2. The secondary zone is well below one standard deviation from the norm, indicating problems attaching meaning to auditory stimuli in a linguistic modality.

3. The tertiary zone is more than two standard deviations below the mean, significantly discrepant from the secondary zone.

4. Memory is approximately age commensurate; word retrieval is a significant problem.

5. Chris is struggling with language processing, even at the beginning levels of attaching meaning. His integrated tertiary zone skills are extremely weak, since his secondary zone language processing is so poor. The significant word retrieval problems in accuracy are probably compounding the problem. Chris also seems to demonstrate some language impulsivity, suggested by the fast naming response on the *TWF*, despite not having retrieved the accurate information.

   Chris may be pushing his system, which is already struggling. An important assessment to add would be a *PPVT* or *ROWPVT* to check language acquisition. The language developmental age that a vocabulary test shows would be the beginning level to expect processing. For example, if the *PPVT* shows receptive vocabulary to be within one standard deviation of the norm, then a significant language processing disorder is present. If the language developmental age is below age expectations, then the problem might be general language acquisition/language delay that has impacted processing. You can't attach meaning to language terms that haven't been acquired.

Case 5: Cassie

Chronological Age: 8.7

Test Results

ITPA	Raw Score	Age Score	Scaled Score
Auditory Closure	11	4-6	15
Sound Blending	5	3-8	21
Sequential Memory	17	4-10	27

LPT	Age Equivalency	Percentile Rank	Standard Score
	below norms	1	57

TOPS—Revised	Age Equivalency	Percentile Rank	Standard Score
	6-1	2	56

TWF			
	Standard Score	By Age: <73	By Grade: <70
	Percentile Rank	By Age: < 4	By Grade: < 2
	Word Finding Profile: Fast & Inaccurate		

Interpretation Questions

1. Are there problems/concerns about the primary zone? (Auditory Closure & Sound Blending)

2. Are there problems/concerns about the secondary zone? (*LPT*)

3. Are there problems/concerns about the tertiary zone? (*TOPS—Revised*)

4. Adjunct areas: any memory or word retrieval influence on results?
    (Sequential Memory & *TWF*)

5. Are there other referrals or areas to pursue in further assessment? What areas in the
    processing hierarchy are probably intact or in deficit?

(See answers on the next page.)

Case 5: Cassie

1. Primary zone is very poor; central auditory processing skills are questionable.

2. Secondary zone processing is significantly discrepant at more than two standard deviations below the norm.

3. Tertiary zone functioning is also more than two standard deviations from the norm, but commensurate with secondary zone skills.

4. Cassie's memory is weak; her word retrieval is also significantly discrepant.

5. Cassie presents challenges all through the processing hierarchy. An important piece of diagnostic information would be to evaluate her language developmental age with a *PPVT* and use that as a comparison for the degree of discrepancy. The severity of Cassie's processing disorder should be interpreted based on her IQ level. Certainly CAP should be screened and considered for assessment referral. Her auditory system is not working well as a modality for meaningful interpretation of information.

Case 6: Kyle

Chronological Age: 8.0

Test Results

ITPA	Raw Score	Age Score	Scaled Score
Auditory Closure	22	7-11	34
Sound Blending	26	above norms	42
Sequential Memory	34	above norms	39

LPT	Age Equivalency	Percentile Rank	Standard Score
	7-9	43	97

TOPS—Revised	Age Equivalency	Percentile Rank	Standard Score
	7-8	31	95

TWF			
	Standard Score	By Age: 79	By Grade: 86
	Percentile Rank	By Age: 8	By Grade: 17
	Word Finding Profile: Fast & Inaccurate		

Interpretation Questions

1. Are there problems/concerns about the primary zone? (Auditory Closure & Sound Blending)

2. Are there problems/concerns about the secondary zone? (*LPT*)

3. Are there problems/concerns about the tertiary zone? (*TOPS—Revised*)

4. Adjunct areas: any memory or word retrieval influence on results?
   (Sequential Memory & *TWF*)

5. Are there other referrals or areas to pursue in further assessment? What areas in the processing hierarchy are probably intact or in deficit?

(See answers on the next page.)

Case 6: Kyle

1. Primary zone skills are strong.

2. Secondary zone skills are commensurate with expectations.

3. Tertiary zone skills are commensurate with age and secondary zone performance.

4. Memory is fine. Word retrieval is a problem.

5. Kyle is able to compensate for retrieval problems by going slowly. When pushed on the *TWF*, he went fast and compromised accuracy. Good auditory skills and memory to hang on to information long enough to attach meaning are helping Kyle compensate.

   It might be beneficial to teach Kyle some compensatory strategies to facilitate retrieval so he doesn't become frustrated and go too fast, compromising his performance. He might also experience some difficulty in academics as the pace picks up in higher grades.

Case 7: Chip

Chronological Age: 8.3

Test Results

ITPA	Raw Score	Age Score	Scaled Score
Auditory Closure	16	5-6	25
Sound Blending	10	5-6	24
Sequential Memory	15	4-5	26

LPT	Age Equivalency	Percentile Rank	Standard Score
	6-7	20	85

TOPS—Revised	Age Equivalency	Percentile Rank	Standard Score
	7-5	28	92

TWF			
	Standard Score	By Age: 99	By Grade: 103
	Percentile Rank	By Age: 48	By Grade: 58
	Word Finding Profile: Fast & Accurate		

Interpretation Questions

1. Are there problems/concerns about the primary zone? (Auditory Closure & Sound Blending)

2. Are there problems/concerns about the secondary zone? (*LPT*)

3. Are there problems/concerns about the tertiary zone? (*TOPS—Revised*)

4. Adjunct areas: any memory or word retrieval influence on results?
   (Sequential Memory & *TWF*)

5. Are there other referrals or areas to pursue in further assessment? What areas in the processing hierarchy are probably intact or in deficit?

(See answers on the next page.)

Case 7: Chip

1. Primary zone skills are poor, leading to questions regarding CAP.

2. Secondary zone skills are weak, measuring on the borderline of one standard deviation from the mean.

3. Tertiary zone skills are fine.

4. Memory is poor, but word retrieval is good.

5. There is no denying that memory could be contributing to Chip's deficits in these results, but his auditory functional skills are very weak, and Chip is not able to compensate, as he did in tertiary zone skills when visual stimuli was added. *SCAN* or other primary zone tests should be done, with probable referral to an audiologist for CAP assessment. The degree of secondary zone deficit will be easier to sort out with CAP results, but Chip's discrete language skills should be reinforced. The subtest of breakdown on the *LPT* would be important for interpretation since Chip's overall test performance was borderline.

Case 8: Ryan

Chronological Age: 9-5

Test Results

ITPA	Raw Score	Age Score	Scaled Score
Auditory Closure	23	8-3	35
Sound Blending	28	above norms	43
Sequential Memory	39	above norms	42

LPT	Age Equivalency	Percentile Rank	Standard Score
	7-8	25	89

TOPS—Revised	Age Equivalency	Percentile Rank	Standard Score
	8-6	31	95

TWF			
	Standard Score	By Age: 102	By Grade: 107
	Percentile Rank	By Age: 56	By Grade: 67
	Word Finding Profile: Slow & Accurate		

Interpretation Questions

1. Are there problems/concerns about the primary zone? (Auditory Closure & Sound Blending)

2. Are there problems/concerns about the secondary zone? (*LPT*)

3. Are there problems/concerns about the tertiary zone? (*TOPS—Revised*)

4. Adjunct areas: any memory or word retrieval influence on results?
   (Sequential Memory & *TWF*)

5. Are there other referrals or areas to pursue in further assessment? What areas in the processing hierarchy are probably intact or in deficit?

(See answers on the next page.)

Case 8: Ryan

1. Primary zone skills look strong and don't appear to be a problem.

2. Secondary zone skills are within one standard deviation, but weak.

3. Tertiary zone skills are fine; stronger than secondary zone performance.

4. Memory is fine. Word retrieval is a problem, but Ryan is compensating well by going slowly.

5. Ryan has some beginning discrepancies, but is compensating well by relying on his strong central auditory skills and memory. A more complex secondary zone assessment might be beneficial, such as *The Listening Test*, to compare Ryan's secondary zone language processing performance on less discrete tasks than the *LPT*. While Ryan's performance is within normal limits, it is discrepant when compared to the level of functioning in other areas and might be worth addressing to prevent escalation of the problem in later years.

****

How did you do? I hope it became clearer as you moved through the cases how to use the assessment results to infer performance back to the neurological model for processing. The language diagnostic process is not as obvious as the audiological assessment because so many variables influencing language processing performance are introduced. However, it helps to proceed cautiously when diagnosing processing deficits to be sure other contributing variables have been controlled within an assessment process.

A careful diagnostic process is critical to effective intervention. When aspects of processing are not discretely evaluated, therapy time can be wasted, resulting in frustration for both the client and clinician. Some of the principles introduced in assessment will continue to be developed as we begin to discuss remediation.

Summary Chart of Case Interpretations

Case #	CAP/Primary	Secondary	Tertiary	Memory	Retrieval
1	Okay	Okay	?	Problem	Okay
2	?	Okay	Problem	Okay	Okay
3	?	?	Okay	Problem	Okay
4	Okay	Problem	Problem	Okay	Problem
5	Problem	Problem	Problem	Problem	Problem
6	Okay	Okay	Okay	Okay	Problem
7	Problem	?	Okay	Problem	Okay
8	Okay	?	Okay	Okay	Problem

Processing Assessment Outline

A. Peripheral auditory assessment—prerequisite to CAP
   1. Pure-tone audiometry
   2. Speech audiometry
   3. Immittance measures
      a. Typanometry
      b. Acoustic reflexes
B. Central auditory processing assessment (CANS/first functional unit)
   1. Monaural
   2. Dichotic
   3. Binaural
   4. Electrophysiological
C. Functional auditory processing assessment (CAP & LP overlap—Heschl's gyrus, second functional unit—primary zone)
   1. Auditory analysis
   2. Auditory association
   3. Auditory attention
   4. Auditory blending /synthesis
   5. Auditory closure
   6. Auditory discrimination
   7. Auditory figure-ground
   8. Auditory localization
   9. Auditory sequencing
D. Language processing assessment—second & third functional units
   1. Secondary zone temporal lobe
      a. Receptive vocabulary test
      b. *Language Processing Test*—discrete language tasks
      c. Concept development
      d. Adjunct areas
         (1) Memory
         (2) Word retrieval
   2. Tertiary zone temporal lobe/third functional unit
      a. Problem solving reasoning
      b. Listening comprehension
      c. Integrated language tasks

Chapter 6: Remediation for Auditory Processing Disorders

Successful intervention for auditory processing deficits depends on careful diagnostic assessment of the disorder. If a child comes to a speech-language pathologist with a diagnostic label, it is important to review the evaluation procedures that were used to determine the label. Without an understanding of the Processing Continuum Model that has been explained previously in this book, a professional could be writing and working on intervention goals that target the wrong area. The following example clarifies the importance of using the Processing Continuum Model in discriminating the level of breakdown.

> A child came with a diagnosis of Central Auditory Processing Disorder (CAPD). As I reviewed assessment results, the tests that reflected poor performance were the *Language Processing Test* and the *Token Test*. The child appeared to be experiencing difficulty with auditory memory when conceptual language was involved (as in the *Token Test*) and attaching meaning within the language code (as in the *Language Processing Test*). Performance on the dichotic auditory tests was within normal limits, and reported that way, but the diagnosis was CAPD! It appeared that the testing audiologist evaluated the entire processing continuum, but included it all under CAPD disorders and did not transition into an acknowledgment of language processing at some point. In fact, good CAP assessment minimizes the role of attention and language.

This assumption is rampant within the field of communication disorders. A clear differential diagnosis between auditory processing and language processing is, unfortunately, rare. The problem occurs when intervention is initiated. Working on signal enhancement strategies with the child described above would not effectively address the problem. The difficulty was occurring after receiving the signal; the problem was attaching linguistic meaning to the signal.

This is one of the major weaknesses in the area of processing. Audiologists conduct the assessment for the CAP component on the processing continuum, but return to the speech-language pathologist for treatment. At present, there are no known medical treatments; treatment models are behavioral. Consequently, remediation for processing deficits should be transdisciplinary, with careful discussion between the audiologist and speech-language pathologist regarding deficit areas.

Recommendations for intervention should focus in two primary areas: compensatory strategies and addressing specific auditory skills. Research in neuroplasticity demonstrates that if the brain is stimulated, it will adapt. Using the top-down and bottom-up theoretical models, bottom-up intervention repetitively drills the skill area to change the behavioral response positively. Top-down therapy introduces global strategies and compensatory techniques to function more effectively. The more global compensatory strategies will be introduced first in the following discussion.

Compensatory Strategies

It is not possible to change or repair a malfunctioning auditory neurological tract for transferring auditory stimuli from the inner ear to the upper cortex. What *can* be accomplished is implementing modifications to enhance, supplement, or clarify the auditory signal so subsequent processing can occur. The goal in compensating is to enhance the signal or modify the environment to insure that the auditory signal is received accurately in the cortex. Some audiologists, such as Jeanane Ferre, divide the compensatory strategies into two areas: direct signal modifications and environmental modifications. Most auditory processing texts and articles list suggestions for modifications. Some of those lists can be overwhelming when presented to a teacher with nothing more than a request to implement the strategies listed. An explanation of how, why, when, etc., needs to accompany the list. It's also important to sort through a generic list of suggestions and determine which are particularly effective for an individual child with a CAPD disorder.

Teacher Modification Strategies for CAPD

The following section lists the most pertinent compensatory strategies for helping a child with CAPD function effectively within an educational setting. An explanation of each item follows to further clarify the intention and insure appropriate implementation of the modification technique.

Teacher Modification Strategies for CAPD

1. Amplify the auditory signal.
2. Reduce extraneous background noises.
3. Allow preferential seating to maximize auditory and visual signals.
4. Simplify verbal instructions; include only pertinent content.
5. Insure the child's attention before beginning verbal instruction.
6. Restate, paraphrase, and emphasize important information.
7. Monitor use of rate, inflection, gestures, etc., to enhance clarity of verbal presentation.
8. Use visual materials and physical demonstration to supplement auditory instruction.
9. Ask questions to check comprehension of material presented.
10. Use a peer-pairing or buddy system to check notes, assignments, etc.

---

1. Amplify the auditory signal.

There are many alternatives available to increase the loudness of the teacher's auditory signal while minimizing background noise, such as an FM system to improve the speech-noise ratio for the child or other assistive listening devices. Headphones can insure increased amplification for reception of the teacher's voice, while also blocking out surrounding noise.

2. Reduce extraneous background noises.

Before beginning verbal instruction, scan the classroom for sources of background noise that could be reduced or eliminating before beginning to talk. Fans might need to be turned off, the door to the hallway closed, windows by the playground closed, or a group project stopped until later. Any background noise will compete with the teacher's voice for signal reception in the child's auditory neurological system.

3. Allow preferential seating.

To maximize auditory and visual signals, the child should be seated close to the area of verbal instruction. One teacher had been told to provide preferential seating by allowing the child to sit in front, which the teacher did—but she taught from the back of the room! This is an example of implementing a modification without understanding its intention. The preferential seating should be in close proximity to where the teacher provides instruction. This placement will limit the amount of extraneous stimuli accompanying the auditory signal. Preferential seating also means positioning the teacher and/or child to limit other distractions, such as a clear view of the playground or street outside the window; facing a colorful, arresting bulletin board; or sitting in the glare of the sun or the light from an overhead projector.

4. Simplify verbal instructions; include only pertinent content.

Limit the amount of information in each instruction. I have heard teachers present a lecture in one long sentence! It is important to present short, focused directions when giving assignments or summarizing information. Divide complex instruction or material into parts using numbers or steps. Shorten sentences and use less complex vocabulary to describe tasks. When clarifying or responding to a question, keep the answer focused and direct. Limit off-target tangents or acknowledge them as such.

5. Insure the child's attention before beginning verbal instruction.

Use attention-getting devices, such as calling the student's name, telling everyone to "listen" or "pay attention" before pertinent information (e.g., assignment), and using a physical touch or cue word. It might also be important to wait until the class has quieted down before beginning to talk.

6. Restate, paraphrase, and emphasize important information.

Auditory stimuli is presented and dissipates; it lacks the redundancy or permanence of written material. Consequently, it is important for the teacher to emphasize important verbal material with auditory redundancy. Repeat important information. Have the students repeat it after you. Review old material before adding new to insure appropriate focus. Relate the old and new material. Use examples to apply and illustrate the information. Rephrase material that is complex or abstract. Use verbal markers and stress to emphasize content, such as "This is important."

7. Monitor use of rate, inflection, gestures.

Use body language, facial expression, verbal emphasis, and gestures to clarify content. Alter the inflection, pitch, speaking rate, and volume of your voice to emphasize key words and emotional content. Pace the lecture with pauses between meaningful units to allow time for assimilation and comprehension. Watch the students for signs of confusion, lack of concentration, or frustration. Speak clearly and naturally without using exaggerated inflection, gestures, or expressions that distract from the auditory signal.

8. Use visual materials and physical demonstration.

Technology has significantly expanded and improved the methods available to supplement verbal presentation of material in a classroom setting. Use the technology available, such as a projected computer screen, an overhead projector, or a chalkboard to outline key points. Write important words, concepts, and assignments on the board or overhead. Demonstrate or physically illustrate points whenever possible. Use pictures and objects to accompany verbal instruction. Associate events from the students' lives and your own experiences to enhance relevance in processing. Use hands-on simulations and projects to improve meaning. When teaching, supplement verbal material with written material whenever possible. Provide study guides at the beginning of a unit. Distribute a printed list of vocabulary words that will be introduced in the lecture. Provide a written outline of the lecture. Back up auditory information in other modalities as often as possible to minimize errors in content received.

9. Ask questions to check comprehension of material presented.

Don't wait until an exam to determine that a student has not received and processed accurate information. Formulate questions for the students to think about and answer as the information is presented. Ask quick quiz questions, checking the *who, what, when, where,* and *how* facts for basic comprehension. Give the child time to think and respond to auditory instructions or questions. Promote visual imaging of verbal content presented by suggesting that students draw mental pictures of what they hear. Encourage questions, discussion, and class comments for active participation in learning.

10. Use a peer-pairing or buddy system.

It isn't always realistic for the teacher to stop and consistently check a student's comprehension of auditory content for the day. A useful strategy is to provide a peer who the student with CAPD can access whenever he or she has questions or wants to check the accuracy of material. The peer could also be assigned to copy lecture notes, check accuracy of a homework assignment sheet before leaving for the day, etc. This assistance relieves some of the everyday burden from the teacher but insures that the student doesn't go too long before someone checks the accuracy of reception for important information.

Student Modification Strategies for CAPD

It is also important to work with the student who has a central auditory processing disorder so that use of the modifications listed can be effective. The student with CAPD must assume some responsibility for dealing with personal auditory difficulties. Introducing self-help strategies through personal organization, checklists, and specific teacher requests can be effective in making sure environmental modifications take place. Compensatory techniques to introduce or teach to the student include the list in the box on page 119, explained in the following listing.

1. Watch and use visual cues to supplement auditory information.

Teach the student the importance of using visual cues to clarify distorted auditory stimuli. Watching a person's face provides cues for visual formation of sounds, emotional impact through facial expression, and relevance of content through body posture and gestures. Many times a compromised auditory signal can be filled in using visual cues to supplement the missed information.

Student Modification Strategies for CAPD

1. Watch and use visual cues to supplement auditory information.

2. Listen for meaning rather than word-for-word repetition.

3. Use the rehearsal technique of repeating information to compensate for poor memory or signal reception.

4. Desensitize to background noise.

5. Learn to concentrate carefully on the speaker.

6. Paraphrase and check comprehension frequently.

7. Ask clarification questions rather than open-ended questions.

8. Use peers to check notes and assignments when given.

9. Tape record to provide redundancy for lecture presentations.

10. Maintain a positive attitude and an active learner role.

2. Listen for meaning rather than word-for-word repetition.

Teach students that it is not important to hear and process every sound or word uttered by a teacher or speaker. We often address this idea in note-taking strategies, such as *Don't write down every word the teacher says. Write the important words or meaningful words that should be remembered. Every* "the" *is not critical!* When listening, a student shouldn't fill up his or her memory loop with word-for-word memorization of the teacher's words. The student should learn to listen for meaning and remember content rather than specific, verbatim lessons.

3. Use the rehearsal technique of repeating information.

Poor memory or distorted signals take longer to process, or extract meaning from, than those received intactly. An excellent strategy is to repeat over and over what a teacher said until you have attached meaning to the unit or written down the notes to process later. Rehearsal is a strategy to keep the memory loop fresh (short-term memory) until it has been processed for meaning.

4. Desensitize to background noise.

The student might have to be exposed to background noise of various types (music, static, conversation, etc.) in a gradual controlled manner while engaged in a learning task to learn how to tune out distractions and concentrate on a primary auditory stimulus. The better the student's ability to maintain focus in the presence of distractions, the less susceptible the student will be to environmental distractions.

5. Learn to concentrate carefully on the speaker.

This skill is paired with some of the strategies already mentioned; however, the ability to maintain focused attention is critical to effective learning, especially with CAPD. A student with CAPD who also has an attention deficit will really struggle in an academic setting. A student must learn to anticipate and concentrate on content and the speaker, blocking out other thoughts and distractions, such as visual stimuli, physical proximity issues with other students, and background noises.

6. Paraphrase and check comprehension frequently.

A student should learn to take notes and rehearse verbal content being presented by translating the information into his own words. The ability to paraphrase generally assists meaningful comprehension of academic material. Encourage the student to use peers to see if their interpretation of content matches the student's with CAPD.

7. Ask clarification questions rather than open-ended questions.

When confused, students are sometimes afraid to ask questions because it might aggravate the teacher. A good strategy is to refine the type of question asked. For example, if a student says, "I don't understand what you're talking about," she is likely to receive a chilly reception from the teacher. A more specific question might be received more positively by the teacher, such as "I understand ____, but I became confused at this point." This kind of question focuses the teacher on a specific content point rather than implying that the whole lecture has been missed. It also serves to verify the content prior to the point of confusion.

8. Use peers to check notes and assignments when given.

A student should be encouraged, not discouraged, from accessing peers to check the accuracy of information received. A student can be given the responsibility to maintain a checklist for assignments, which can be reviewed by another student. Notes can be compared for inclusion of major content points. Information that wasn't clearly received can be marked to clarify with a peer rather than the teacher. These strategies teach the student to assume more independence in compensating for the CAPD disorder and free the teacher from regular monitoring responsibilities.

9. Tape record to provide redundancy for lecture presentations.

A good way to make sure that verbal presentations in the classroom are accurately received and processed for notes is to tape record them for later listening. Replaying the tape allows the student to pause and slow down the rate of presentation while taking notes or trying to assimilate meaning to the auditory material. The tape provides an auditory record of lecture information for the student.

10. Maintain a positive attitude and an active learner role.

Teach the student specific organizational strategies that get him ready to listen effectively. He should be a proactive learner, reviewing content prior to the verbal lecture or presentation by the teacher. He should actively participate in discussion with comments and questions to insure accurate reception and comprehension of material as it is presented. His body posture and facial expression should communicate focused attention to the teacher. Difficulties or confusion should be clarified as soon as convenient, rather than waiting until just before an examination. The student's assumption of learning responsibilities will make a teacher more receptive to working with the student to implement compensatory recommendations.

Specific Skill Strategies

There are a variety of ways to approach actual remediation of the auditory skills involved in accurate reception of auditory signals. Most of the published materials divide into two categories: those addressing features of the actual acoustic signal and those addressing specific, functional auditory tasks in the overlap area on the continuum.

Acoustic Feature Skill Intervention

Most of the remedial programs that focus on detection of the signal are based in Paula Tallal's research efforts. Over the decades, Tallal and her colleagues investigated the smallest unit of processing and the temporal aspects of signal detection. Much of her work resulted in the assumption that individuals with CAPD cannot process acoustic stimuli at the typical rate of presentation. The timing or rate of an acoustic stimulus has direct bearing on the ability to accurately perceive and respond to the acoustic stimulus.

The very early intervention efforts in this area could be categorized within the lip-reading exercises. Individuals were taught to watch speech being produced to recognize the motor production patterns as sounds and words were formed. While shortcomings were obvious (speaker with back to listener, movements masked by moustaches and beards, etc.), instructors teach the listener with auditory problems to supplement compromised auditory signals with visual cues.

Phonetic context drill books were also a good source of remediation exercises for students with central auditory processing disorders. While the problem wasn't based in specific articulation or production deficits, the controlled contrast pairs were effective tools for teaching improved auditory awareness of the acoustic features of sounds.

One of the first central auditory processing remedial programs to emerge based on accuracy of the signal detected was authored by Christine Sloan (1986). Dr. Sloan drilled the child with CAPD to discriminate differences between speech sounds through verbal presentation. Contrast and context were two of the critical features in how sounds were chosen and presented to improve auditory perception. Extensive data was collected to record progress accountably.

The child was bombarded with syllables, varied by a chosen target of phonetic contrast. The contrast could be a consonant or a vowel, depending on the target context. The child was to identify the target syllable as presented in multiple phonetic repetitions. For example, if the goal was perception of the /de/-/te/ contrast, the child would hear multiple repetitions of the two, with a goal to identify the target whenever it occurred.

The more current technology that has been introduced to accomplish very similar skill drill is the *Fast ForWord* (Scientific Learning Corporation) computer program. Original authors were Drs. Michael Merzenich and Paula Tallal. Dr. Merzenich's research focused on brain plasticity and learning. Dr. Tallal's work concentrated on the temporal aspects of sound recognition. The two professionals combined their research areas to devise a CD-Rom computer program comprised of a series of exercises to modify the rate of acoustic stimuli to gradually strengthen neural pathways involved in sound recognition.

The specific auditory skills drilled in the *Fast ForWord* exercises include signal detection, recognition, discrimination, memory, and sequencing. The phonemic and timing aspects of primarily consonant-vowel syllables are acoustically manipulated to slow down until the child can detect the acoustic features accurately—and then gradually increased until a normal timing pattern is accomplished.

For central auditory processing disorders, the *Fast ForWord* program makes sense. The approach is founded in bottom-up theories of processing that believe meaning cannot be attached to an acoustic stimulus unless the acoustic features of the signal can be discriminated. Many children who struggle with reading deficits do not have a solid phonetic foundation for acoustic discrimination of sounds. The program, however, makes far-reaching promises of success in areas of language processing and academic learning that continue to be debated. Functional application of meaning to the acoustic stimulus introduced is extremely limited in the *Fast ForWord* program, and success in more applied use of acoustic stimuli has been variable.

Earobics is another auditory program that has been developed to train improved listening skills in children through a series of drilled exercises. *Earobics* allows a speech-language pathologist more control in determining components of the program, as opposed to *Fast ForWord*, which is pre-programed and arrives via the CD-rom internet connection.

Many of the phonic approach remediation programs can also be used with CAPD students to develop increased awareness of acoustic features of the various consonants and vowels in the language system. Other programs continue to be developed, some using computer technology, others tape and CD technology, while others rely on the speech-language pathologist to introduce the acoustic stimuli for training and discrimination.

The important variable in choosing a skill approach to CAPD is to determine which aspects of the acoustic signal's reception are being addressed or drilled in the program. The early part of the processing continuum relies on very pure signal transference through the auditory channels and trying to strengthen those neurological pathways requires fairly discrete input and output.

Examples of specific discrete, acoustic-feature drill tasks are listed below.

Discrete, Acoustic-Feature Drill Tasks

Task	Example
Phoneme identification	Discriminating /p/ versus /b/ or /e/ versus /i/
Pitch identification	Discriminating high versus low pitches or matching same/different pitch tones
Temporal processing	Acoustically modifying speech until it is discriminated accurately
Pitch pattern identification	Discriminating the presentation order of different tones

---

Functional Auditory Skills

Auditory processing that occurs at the level of the cortex involves receipt of the acoustic signal as well as rudimentary processing for meaning or recognition of a linguistic message encoded. These auditory skills were included in the transition phase on the Processing Continuum Model, where both auditory and language processing are jointly engaged, auditory processing at ending levels and language processing at beginning levels.

The compensatory strategies explained previously also address the level of functional auditory skills. The discrete auditory skills to drill in intervention outlined in this section become more language-code based, rather than simple acoustic features of the signal (pitch, volume, and rate). Many of these auditory skills have a significant impact on academic learning in the areas of phonics for reading, spelling, and eventually comprehension. However, it is important when conducting treatment exercises for these auditory skills to keep the tasks as discrete as possible and not compound them with academic knowledge or language concepts.

Ten common functional auditory skills are listed below and followed with explanations and examples to illustrate them. Remedial goals could target any of these skills specifically. Extensive resources are available to save speech-language pathologists time in generating lists of drill materials to remediate these discrete auditory skill areas. Since definitions can vary by author, professionals should carefully examine materials labeled as addressing one of these tasks to see if the tasks are consistent with the definitions provided in this section.

Functional Auditory Processing Skills

1. Auditory Analysis/Segmentation
2. Auditory Attention
3. Auditory Association
4. Auditory Closure
5. Auditory Discrimination
6. Auditory Figure-Ground
7. Auditory Localization
8. Auditory Memory
9. Auditory Sequential Memory
10. Auditory Synthesis/Sound Blending/Auditory Closure

---

1. Auditory Analysis/Segmentation

Auditory analysis is a skill to break a word down into its individual sounds or syllables. A whole is broken down into its specific segments by extracting or analyzing the individual sounds or syllables. Lists of words would be presented with the child being asked to discriminate a specific sound segment from each word presented. Various possible tasks to address deficits in this auditory skill are listed in the box below with an example for each one.

Auditory Analysis/Segmentation Tasks

Example Task Presentation	Response
Identify the first/initial sound you hear in the word *cat*.	/k/
Identify the last/final sound you hear in the word *make*.	/k/
Identify the vowel you hear in the word *hot*.	/a/
Identify the first/initial syllable in the word *father*.	/fa/
Identify the middle syllable in the word *telephone*.	-/lɛ/
Identify the last/final syllable in the word *telephone*.	-/fon/
How many sounds are in the word *test*? Begin with one-syllable words with spelling corresponding to sounds. Progress to words where spelling does not represent sounds, such as *pie (*2 sounds). Progress to two-syllable and multisyllabic words.	4
What sounds are in the word *mop*? Begin with one-syllable words where spelling and sounds match. Progress to spelling and sound differences such as *clock* (/k/, /l/, /a/, /k/). Progress to two-syllable and multi-syllabic words.	/m/, /a/, /p/

---

2. Auditory Attention

Auditory attention is defined as being aware of specific sounds and attending to them for an appropriate length of time. This skill is most critical for speech signals. It is difficult to drill auditory attention by itself or for its own sake because a child needs something to pay attention to before attention will be gained or is necessary. Language comprehension also tends to minimize auditory attention. A child who is confused, overwhelmed, or frustrated will stop paying attention to auditory stimuli and tune it out.

The role of attention cannot be overemphasized in processing and learning. Attention to information is required to decode incoming stimuli and encode information for storage in memory. Biological factors can enhance attention, such as movement, contrast, and strength of a stimulus. The two factors that determine attention are the brain's chemicals and the sensory input of the stimulus. The chemical factor is addressed through compensatory techniques of insuring a biological awareness and alertness. A teacher can monitor the saliency of sensory input, but a child can learn to improve focused attention also.

The easiest way to work on improving auditory attention is to provide a pleasant, interesting or motivating stimulus for the child. Over time, decrease the movement and variety of stimuli to primarily auditory input. Gradually lengthen the auditory message or content presented to stretch the child's auditory focused attention. Tasks can become more academic in nature by doing worksheets in which directions must be listened to and followed to accurately complete the task. Some examples are provided below.

Auditory Attention Tasks

Read a story with pictures, asking questions to check comprehension every page, then every two pages. Then lengthen time between questions.

Have an art, snack, or science activity that the child completes by following one-step directions.

Present a puzzle worksheet that is completed by following verbal directions.

(continued on the next page)

127

Increase directions from one critical element to two, three, and four as the child experiences success; for example:

1. Color the <u>ball</u>.
2. Color the <u>big ball</u>.
3. Color the <u>big ball green</u>.
4. Color the <u>big ball with green stripes</u>.

3. Auditory Association

Auditory association as an auditory discrete skill is the ability to match an acoustic stimulus with its source. When a noise is heard, a child needs to determine what is generating that noise to discriminate if it is important to pay attention to.

Some professionals include phoneme sound-symbol relationships under the area of auditory association. Drill in this auditory task would progress from environmental noise association by sound, and then to letter association by sound. Some of the phonemic awareness tasks could fit under this skill area if that more general definition is applied. Some examples are listed below.

Auditory Association Tasks

Match a sound with its source. Display objects on a table. The child closes his eyes. Make noise with one of the objects. Then the child opens his eyes and picks the object that made the noise.

Identify what makes a sound. Begin with live presentation in the room and pictures of the sound makers. Blow a whistle, for example, and have the child identify the source of the sound (a whistle). Progress to *dog, doorbell, siren,* and *telephone* using taped sounds with corresponding pictures.

Identify a sound from an audiotape presentation; tell what makes that sound.

Identify the source of sounds. Looking at a picture of a room and hearing a taped noise, identify what/where in the room the sound is coming from.

(continued on the next page)

128

Ask questions about sound-symbol associations, such as these:

What letter would make this sound? /b/ (the letter B/b)

What sound would this letter (point to M) make? (/m/)

4. Auditory Closure

Auditory closure is the ability to fill in missing or distorted auditory information. Sounds that are absent or compromised within a word or sentence can throw off the listener when he is trying to abstract meaning from an acoustic signal. The ability to replace or fill in missing sounds allows the child to "close" the auditory signal. Auditory closure is a fairly sophisticated skill that requires active listening and integration with vocabulary knowledge and context cues to fill in missing acoustic pieces.

The *Illinois Test of Psycholinguistic Abilities* was among the first to present tasks in the area of auditory closure. Drilling the skill in deficit entails deleting sounds from a word to see if the student can fill in or close the auditory sequence to identify the target word. Present words with a natural inflection and prosody; rate and flow should not be slowed down, overemphasized, or articulated in an exaggerated manner. Some examples of different tasks follow below. The student is asked to identify the whole word that is presented incompletely.

Auditory Closure Tasks

Example Auditory Skill Task Presentation	Response
Finish this word for me. The last part is missing. "by-sic-"	bicycle
Fill in the middle of this word. "bah-____-le "	bottle
Tell me what the word is by filling in the first part. "ensil"	pencil
Fill in missing pieces of this phrase. "peanut -utter and -elly"	peanut butter and jelly

5. Auditory Discrimination

Auditory discrimination is the ability to distinguish between sounds. Many language sounds are acoustically similar. A child must learn to hear the similarities and differences between sounds to accurately identify words presented orally. Auditory discrimination generally focuses more on phoneme discrimination, but it can also include discrimination of other acoustic features, such as pitch or tone, volume, or environmental sounds.

Auditory discrimination by position or place in a word or syllable can also be included under this discrete skill area. However, if the student is not able to do auditory analysis at the level of understanding initial, medial, or final position in words, discrimination should not be attempted by position.

It is difficult to work on this auditory skill if the child doesn't have the language concept of *likeness* or being able to identify items that match or are the same versus different. It is usually advantageous to begin work on this skill using pictures and larger auditory units, such as words, and gradually progress to sound discrimination. Various auditory discrimination tasks are described below and on page 130.

Auditory Discrimination Tasks

Example Auditory Skill Task Presentation	Response

Identification of words being the same/different with pictures
    Point to the two words you hear me say. You can point to the
    same picture twice. *cat - hat*
	points to *cat + hat*

Are these words the same or different? *lake - lake*	same
Is the first sound in these words the same or different? *pig - pan* Is the last sound in these words the same or different? *mat - lot*	same same
Is the first sound in these syllables the same or different? *by - guy*	different
Is the last sound in these syllables the same or different? *am - im*	same

(continued on the next page)

Is the first sound in these words the same or different? *dine - dollar*	same
Is the last sound in these words the same or different? *rose - bus*	different
Are these notes the same or different? (low tone - high tone)	different
Are these words the same loudness or different? (loud - soft)	different

6. Auditory Figure-Ground

Auditory figure-ground is the ability to differentiate a primary auditory stimulus from other background auditory stimuli. This auditory skill is essential for a child to identify the speaker or main auditory signal in a room and tune out or ignore background noises or competing auditory stimuli. For many children, this task involves teaching them to discriminate relevant versus irrelevant auditory stimuli.

Auditory figure-ground can be taught through a series of tasks that gradually desensitize a student to background noises. The student builds a tolerance to distracting acoustic stimuli while learning to consciously focus on the primary auditory stimulus. As the student's figure-ground skills improve, the tasks can increase the challenge presented by the competing auditory stimuli. A sequence of tasks to develop auditory figure-ground skills is listed below and on page 131. Introduce competing noises (white noise, conversation, another speaker) softly at first; increase the volume gradually as the student's figure-ground skills improve.

Auditory Figure-Ground Tasks

Identify an object with a tape of static/white noise playing in the room; for example, "Point to the door."

Recognize a word in the presence of static/white noise; for example, "Say this word. Window."

Do an auditory listening task with instrumental music playing in the background, such as playing "Bingo."

(continued on the next page)

131

Answer simple fact questions with static noise present; for example, "What's your name?" Do an auditory listening task with cafeteria-type general conversation or playground noise in the background, such as playing "Go Fish."

Do an auditory listening task with vocal music playing in the background, such as playing "20 Questions."

Do an auditory listening task with a radio playing with a combination of commercials, music, and talking, such as playing "Trivia."

Do an auditory task while a tape of someone reading a story plays in the background, such as completing a worksheet.

7. Auditory Localization

Auditory localization is the ability to identify where a sound is coming from. Locating the generator of a sound assists a student in knowing how to enhance or magnify an acoustic stimulus by moving toward the source, or conversely, move away from a distracting sound. The specific skill can be drilled to teach a student to tune in more specifically to the environmental source for acoustic information.

The auditory skill of sound localization can be combined with recognition of typical sound sources within an environment (auditory association) to facilitate improved compensatory actions. For example, if a child knows that the blower in a classroom is located in the ceiling above a certain section of desks, he could decide not to sit in that section because a distracting noise is located in that area. Examples of activities to address auditory localization skill development are listed below.

Auditory Localization Tasks

Stand behind the child and ring a bell. Ask, "Where is the noise coming from?"

Blindfold the child or have her close her eyes and turn her body toward a sound's source.

Hide a ticking clock in the room and ask the child to find the source of the ticking.

Have the child find sources of sound/noise in the room and tell whether they are positive or distracting noise sources.

8. Auditory Memory

Auditory memory involves remembering acoustic information that was presented. Short term auditory memory is retaining what was just heard, while long term auditory memory is the ability to retrieve stored information presented previously. Short term memory has more significant bearing on auditory processing and is the focus here. Long term memory is closely integrated and influenced by language processing and is addressed in the next chapter.

Short-term memory is also called *working memory* and involves retention of information for approximately 5-20 seconds. Auditory information tends to fade quickly. It will not be retained unless the acoustic stimulus is refreshed through rehearsal or repetition, or is stored in long-term memory for later recall. If a child cannot retain acoustic information long enough to analyze the signal and extract meaning from it, then the rest of the processing continuum will be compromised. We already talked about the importance of using visual stimuli to back up auditory information and compensate for CAPD. This is an attempt to strengthen the discrete auditory memory skill.

Auditory Memory Tasks

Remember an identified component, such as "Remember the **first**/last/middle word I say. **desk**, tiger, pencil" (desk)

Remember an identified word; for example, "Every time you hear the word *brown* in the story, clap your hands. Brown Bear, Brown Bear, ..."

Remember named items; for example, have students each name one item in a category (start with three students and gradually increase the number of players). Use general categories, such as foods, colors, etc. Then have students name one item they remember hearing.

Remember multiple items; follow the same procedure as above, but have each student name as many named category items as he can remember.

Read a sentence and ask basic fact questions, such as "What was the boy's name?"

---

9. Auditory Sequential Memory

Auditory sequential memory is the ability to remember auditory stimuli in the exact order in which they were heard. Auditory sequential memory is usually considered a subskill of auditory memory since short-term memory needs to be fairly intact to retain information presented. Auditory sequential memory involves remembering acoustic information (numbers, tones, letters, words, sounds, rhythms, etc.) in a specific order.

Auditory sequential memory involves the skill of chunking information together in a specific sequence. Sequential memory will be enhanced if meaning is inherent in the pieces. The typical 'chunk' that can be retained without meaning is seven units. That's why ZIP codes, addresses, and phone numbers try to stay under seven numbers—so people can remember them.

Here is an example of meaningful and nonmeaningful acoustic stimuli, although it is in visual form. Read these two items aloud:

car, cookie, arm, leg , frog, chair, pen, key, computer, printer

The dog chased the cat up the oak tree, so the fire department was called to get the cat down.

Now cover up both of the items. Repeat the first list of words. Then repeat the sentence. How did you do?

If you are like most people, you retained about eight words from the list, but may have lost a few and gotten the middle ones out of order. The words that were associated by meaning you probably kept together, such as *arm, leg* and *computer, printer*, as well as the words associated by sound context, such as *car, cookie, key, computer*. However, you were probably able to repeat the entire sentence back perfectly, or maybe with an omission/modification of a few words. The word list has ten items; the sentence has 20 items, double the word list. What's the difference? Context or meaning is involved in the sentence. The words in the sentence hang together and flow, unlike the listed words. This idea will be revisited in Compensatory Strategies in Chapter 7, pages 148-154.

For central auditory processing purposes, we are primarily talking about sequential memory for nonrelated acoustic material. The child needs to achieve a sequential memory length of at least five to seven units to function effectively in the academic setting. Once that level has been achieved, compensatory techniques can be used for more complex signals, such as visual cues, written records, or taped recordings.

Auditory memory can often be facilitated using visual stimuli to supplement the acoustic information. As auditory memory skills improve, the visual stimuli can be faded. Some examples of tasks to remediate short-term auditory sequential memory are listed below.

Auditory Sequential Memory Tasks

Memory for objects	Place three items on a table. Have the child close his eyes and name them in order. Gradually add more items.
Rote sequence with context	Nursery rhymes, poems, finger plays, etc.
Rote sequence in sentences	Read a sentence and have the child repeat it. Gradually increase the sentence length and complexity.
Rote academic sequences	Days, months, counting, alphabet, etc.
Varied rote sequences	Name a letter from the alphabet, such as M, and have the child recite the rest of the alphabet from that point to the end.
Memory for named objects	Name three items. Have the child repeat them.
Memory for numbers, letters, etc.	Gradually increase the number up to ten items.
Memory for sequence	Play "I'm going on a trip and taking a ___."
Memory for non-linguistic auditory stimuli	Reproduce clapping or tapping patterns.
Memory for sounds	Present noises and have the child say what made the sounds in order, such as "bell, whistle, horn, dog."

---

10. Auditory Synthesis/Sound Blending/Auditory Closure

Auditory synthesis is the ability to blend individual sounds together to form words. The child is required to remember sounds that are presented separately, and then combine them together smoothly to create a word. This auditory skill is the opposite of sound analysis, which requires a child to break a word down into its individual sound parts. In this task, a student must synthesize isolated sounds into word units.

Facilitate these tasks by using pictures initially to help the child synthesize sounds. It might also be important to provide visual symbols of the sounds if memory is significantly impaired and the child can't retain the individual sounds that need to be blended. Fade these visual symbols gradually if the child becomes auditorily proficient. The entire word doesn't have to be separated initially; syllables or parts can be joined, with the synthesis task gradually increasing in the number of units to blend.

Auditory Synthesis/Sound Blending Tasks

Identify the picture of the word I am saying. k—ar (car)

Identify the word that these sounds make. h—air (hair)

Put these sounds together to make a word. s—ee (see)
Begin with one-syllable words; progress to two-syllable, to multisyllable; also expand the number of sound segments to be blended.

Applied Auditory Skills

The professional market has expanded significantly in materials and specialized programs designed to address aspects of central auditory processing skills. A few of the more recognized programs or approaches that drill discrete signal detection aspects of a CAPD are listed on page 136.

The area of phonemic awareness is also expanding rapidly. Research and clinical studies have supported the importance of a strong phonemic foundation to bridge into academic success in reading, writing, spelling, and other language-based learning tasks. Many of the phonemic awareness programs contain components that would be beneficial for the student who has CAPD.

Remember that many therapy materials whose titles suggest a focus on *auditory processing* actually incorporate language concepts and address *language processing* rather than auditory processing skills. When trying to decide if a therapy resource addresses central auditory processing, look at the description of tasks. If language concepts, comprehension, problem solving, etc., are involved, then the material targets post-auditory processing on the continuum. Tasks listed should match the ones addressed in this chapter: auditory attention, auditory memory, auditory localization, auditory discrimination, etc.

Materials for Central Auditory Processing Skills Training

Treating Auditory Processing Difficulties in Children by Christine Sloan; Singular Publishing, San Diego, CA.

Earobics; available from Thinking Publications, Eau Claire, WI.

The Lindamood Phoneme Sequencing Program (LiPS) by Patricia and Phyllis Lindamood; Pro-Ed, Austin, TX.

What's That I Hear—Activities to Develop Listening Skills in Children 3-8 by Sam Ed Brown; Communication Skill Builders, Tucson, AZ.

Auditory Processes by Pam Gillet; Academic Therapy Publications, Novato, CA.

The Processing Program by Sandra McKinnis; Thinking Publications, Eau Claire, WI.

The Central Auditory Processing Kit by Mary Ann Mokhemar; LinguiSystems, Inc., East Moline, IL.

Auditory Processing Enhancement Programs and *Perceive and Respond Auditory Program* by Josef. Saunders; Academic Communication Associates, Oceanside, CA.

Fast ForWord, available from Scientific Learning Corporation, Berkeley, CA.

Summary Comments

In conclusion, it is always important to remember the two-pronged approach to remediation for central auditory processing disorders—compensatory strategies and specific skill treatment. When environmental modifications are implemented and specific weaknesses in discrete skills are resolved, most individuals with central auditory processing disorders should function effectively in academic and daily living environments.

Chapter 7: Remediation for Language Processing Disorders

Intervention for language processing disorders parallels the major focus areas of central auditory processing: compensatory strategies and structured intervention for specific language skills in deficit. However, there are two guiding principles that must be in place for language processing remediation to be effective:

1. Remediation must reflect a hierarchical model based on neurological development that builds language skills in a logical sequence of increased cognitive complexity.

2. Use multimodality stimulation to engage the primary and secondary zones of the occipital, parietal, and temporal lobes to process incoming stimuli.

One of the confounding aspects of therapy for language processing has been the lack of a theoretical model guiding the assessment and intervention goals. Speech-language pathologists have pulled language assessment tools off the shelf, administered them to students, and then written goals to address any subtest areas of deficit. Clinicians often didn't know where to start or when to stop when it came to the area of language because they lacked a model to structure intervention. Using other speech-language disorder areas as examples might clarify this problem.

During screening, the speech-language pathologist hears a child speaking and notices that she is difficult to understand. An articulation test is administered, and several sounds are found to be in error. The clinician might generate a long-term goal for the child to correctly produce those phonemes in conversational speech, but therapy isn't initiated at the level of conversational speech. The speech-language pathologist knows that certain skills have to be developed gradually to build up to the coordinated neurological ability to produce the sounds in conversation. Therapy will begin with sounds in isolation, progressing to syllables, to words, to phrases and sentences, and finally to conversation. The intervention is arranged in a sequential hierarchy to establish a new neurological production pattern. Therapy progresses from very isolated, discrete production skills to more integrated, complex articulation production tasks.

Similar hierarchical sequences could be derived for voice, fluency, syntax, and other communication disorders. The assessment task or subtest skill is not where therapy begins and ends. The speech-language pathologist generates and targets a sequence to build up to that communication task.

Language has been the unfortunate exception in communication disorders. For example, when a child misses items on the *Boehm Test of Basic Concepts*, a goal is written to teach those concepts. When all 50 can be marked appropriately on the test form, the child is dismissed, or another language test is given to determine what should be addressed next. Rarely does the speech-language pathologist analyze what language skills the child must master to be ready to handle the 50 Boehm concepts. Maybe the child isn't ready to learn Boehm concepts; the child might need to learn other language skills first. The language processing tasks that are prerequisite to attaining conceptual comprehension should be evaluated and targeted before the Boehm concepts.

A child must learn to walk in language tasks before he can run, shoot, and score! Language develops in a hierarchy of cognitive complexity from simple, discrete language processing into more integrated, complex language processing. Because a child demonstrated errors on a complex language processing task doesn't mean the child is ready to work on that skill. The speech-language pathologist must first evaluate the achieved level of language processing and determine what comes next in the hierarchy of development.

The Processing Continuum Model provides a framework for the hierarchy of language. The ability to attach meaning to acoustic stimuli begins in simple, discrete neurological tasks and gradually increases in complexity. Targeting skills based upon test errors is a poor model for making therapy decisions. It is very hit and miss and can result in a Swiss cheese intervention pattern. I can always tell a child who has had therapy following this random approach to language. The pattern in the child's language skills makes no sense, and the child displays several splintered language processing skills in high levels of complexity, but the language skills supporting the task are incredibly weak. That's what teachers notice. The child seems intelligent and capable but can't consistently perform academic tasks.

So the first guiding principle to think about in language processing remediation is a hierarchical model based on neurological development that guides expectations along a logical continuum of increasing cognitive complexity. Read that sentence again; it is long, but contains the crux of effective language processing therapy. Simply stated, you need a model that defines an order within language tasks to guide therapy from easy, isolated tasks into more complex, integrated tasks, just as in therapy for articulation, phonology, voice, fluency, syntax, etc.— a model that helps the clinician decide where to start, what comes next, and when it is finished.

The second principle that must guide language processing therapy is also based on the neurological Processing Continuum Model. In the processing continuum, the language processing model incorporates the functional units theory. The second functional unit is where language processing occurs. Each lobe (parietal, occipital, temporal) is charged with primary zone reception and processing in a specific sensory modality.

In language processing disorders, there seems to be a neurological glitch in the efficiency of the secondary zone temporal lobe for processing acoustic stimuli. If that area is weak, it doesn't make sense to remediate by working only in the weak area. The theory behind the functional units model is magnified in importance with regard to remediation.

When treating language processing deficits, you want to stimulate or turn on all the secondary zones to use all three processing units and the integration tertiary zone to assist in attaching meaning to the stimulus. If only auditory information is provided, only the primary zone temporal lobe lights up, and that secondary zone is the only one energized to work on the information. If information is presented through multimodality sensation, the whole second functional unit can assist in processing information and help the weak temporal lobe secondary zone. So when auditory information is accompanied by visual and physical cues, the temporal lobe benefits from redundant processing assistance in the occipital and parietal lobes. The primary and secondary zones of the occipital, parietal, and temporal lobes are all engaged in processing the incoming stimulus.

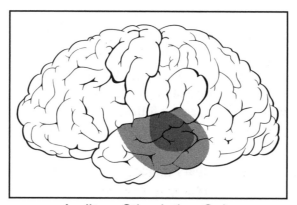

Auditory Stimulation Only

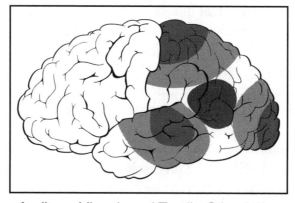

Auditory, Visual, and Tactile Stimulation

With these two principles guiding language processing remediation, we'll begin with an explanation of the more global compensatory strategies. The components introduced in Chapter 3: Language Processing Model will begin to fit together to form an applied remediation model.

In Chapter 5: Processing Assessment, two adjunct areas were highlighted as making significant contributions to language processing: memory and word retrieval. Let's expand on these two areas to further explain their role in processing and their importance in successful compensatory strategies.

Memory

Memory was briefly introduced in the previous chapter within the section addressing functional auditory skills (see pages 124-135). Short term memory was targeted primarily in that area, with long term memory falling under language processing. Memory, both short and long term, play an important role in processing.

Memory is a process; it is not a fixed thing or located at one isolated place in the brain. We have memory for all kinds of stimuli. Nerve cells store memory traces in short or long term memory. When language information needs to be retrieved, neurons trigger memory, so mem-ory and retrieval are intimately connected. The best way to recall information is to trigger associated information connected with it. Understanding how memory is stored will clarify that idea. The diagram below illustrates the steps in memory storage. A brief description of each stage follows the diagram.

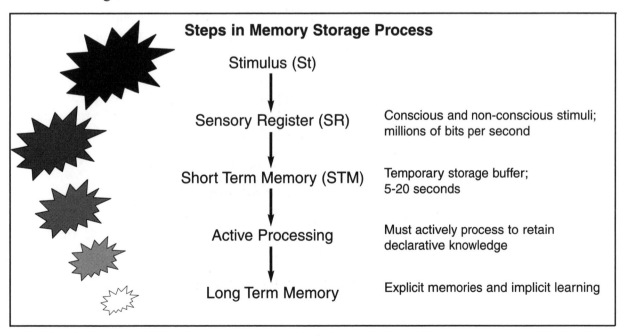

Steps in Memory Storage Process

Stimulus (St)
↓
Sensory Register (SR) — Conscious and non-conscious stimuli; millions of bits per second
↓
Short Term Memory (STM) — Temporary storage buffer; 5-20 seconds
↓
Active Processing — Must actively process to retain declarative knowledge
↓
Long Term Memory — Explicit memories and implicit learning

Stage 1: Stimulus (St)

A stimulus is presented and the neurological system reacts. At the point of presentation, the stimulus is at its strongest, with multiple components all impacting the body: smell, sound, feel, texture, appearance, etc.

Stage 2 - Sensory Register (SR)

The sensory aspects of the stimulus are picked up and registered in an individual's neurological system. The sensory register is bombarded by millions of bits of information per second at an unconscious and a conscious level. Consequently, every aspect of every stimulus does not register at its full potency. The stimulus is diminished somewhat.

Stage 3 - Short Term Memory (STM)

Short term memory is where rudimentary analysis of the incoming sensory information occurs. Short term memory is limited by both capacity (7-10 units) and time (5-20 seconds). Short term memory is also called *working memory* because active processing begins here. It serves as a temporary storage area for shallow processing until decisions are made to "let go" or store the stimulus more permanently. The stimulus continues to diminish in STM because of the limitations.

Stage 4 - Long Term Memory (LTM)

Long term memory is where deeper analysis occurs. Semantic processing requires using stored knowledge and integrating new information with the old. Explicit and implicit memory are influenced by the type of information and experiences associated with the stimulus. Only the more salient aspects of the stimulus will be stored, so the stronger the stimulus initially, the larger the memory trace by association for recall. Novel experiences are more difficult to process because no experiences can be recalled from long term memory to assist the processing task. Familiar information is reinforced by multiple stored memory experiences.

The diagram on page 140 and its explanation should help illustrate how "forgetting" is actually poor retrieval of stored information. Strengthening short term memory to hold on to information long enough to process it was addressed in the previous chapter on pages 132-134. Improving the ability to retrieve stored information from long term memory will be addressed in the next section on word retrieval.

Word Retrieval

The primary behavioral characteristic observed in language processing deficits is word retrieval difficulty. Knowledge is present; the struggle is in accessing it quickly and accurately. If you recall from the case examples in Chapter 5, the two variables evaluated on the *Test of Word Finding* (German) are *accuracy* and *efficiency*. Comprehension is also evaluated. A clinician cannot imply that the problem is retrieval if the language hasn't been acquired yet. But most of the time, the difficulty is in locating the information required in long-term memory.

Let's engage in a few tasks to illustrate this concept, as well as lay the groundwork for compensatory strategies.

Task 1

Get a piece of paper, a pencil, and a stopwatch or something to time one minute. (Do it, I'll wait.)

Now list as many animals as you can think of in one minute. Go! (Think *Jeopardy* music.)

Time's up! Now count how many you came up with. I'll presume accuracy, and I won't check to see if you named animals versus something else.

Now let's talk about the process. If you are like most people completing this task, you started out fine. After about 20 seconds, the names might have slowed down or stopped completely momentarily. That's the key! What did you do at that point in time?

Many of you probably went to a subcategory of animals to "open a new drawer" and refresh the retrieval process. *Farm, zoo, forest, pets, land, sea*, and *air* are subcategory types you might have used to generate more names. You could have delved even further into subcategories of subcategories, such as pets, to dogs, to breeds of dogs.

Perhaps you recalled a recent trip to the zoo and mentally walked through again. That means you used visual images to cue yourself and start the names of animals rolling again while recalling the physical stroll through the zoo.

Some of you might have triggered a new flow of vocabulary by thinking of features of animals, such as fur, wings, and feathers. The color, shape, or size would be another way of using features to prompt retrieval.

143

Phonological cues would involve going through the alphabet or a book of animals naming one for each letter. A high school scientist cued himself by thinking of species (wouldn't work for me!). A sports fan used team mascots to generate his ideas.

Task One Lessons

- Additional knowledge was present, even though the quickness slowed down or stopped momentarily. It didn't mean language knowledge was depleted.

- You knew what to do to cue renewed retrieval of language. You didn't just stop and give up and wait for the minute timer to go off. You had learned strategies that you self-applied to keep yourself productive in the language processing task.

- You might have used other modalities to compensate or help, such as visual images (occipital lobe), tactile features (parietal lobe), or movement (frontal lobe). When one modality hits a snag (temporal lobe), it is natural to access other modalities to help.

Task Two

You all studied states and their capitals. Name the capitals of Illinois and New Mexico.

Having any trouble? What's the problem, didn't you learn that?! Do you feel like the answers are in your memory, but you're going to have to work to get there, and you're not sure if it's worth the effort? Welcome to the world of language processing deficits!

Depending on where you live, one of them might have popped right out, and you are doing a process of elimination on the other one. All right, let's see if they are in there. The beginning letter cue is that both capitals start with *S*. Did that narrow things down to solve it?

Let's start with New Mexico. If you've been there or live nearby, it might not have been a problem. For those less familiar with the state, you might have generated the two main cities, Albuquerque and Santa Fe, and figured it was one of the two. My cue was all you needed to answer *Sante Fe* with confidence.

Illinois might have been easy for Midwestern natives. However, if that's not a familiar area, Chicago might have jumped out, but with question marks as to whether it was the capital. The *S* told you it wasn't and *Springfield* might have triggered from a *Land of Lincoln* association.

Task Two Lessons

- Experience with information makes a difference. Experience has a profound effect on neurological maturation and learning. The foundation and raw materials of neurology for learning can be present, but experience is what fills in the base for more integrated, complex learning.

- The cue of the first letter provided a context to help you sort through the language information you retrieved. Confidence might have increased when that cue proved that you were right. The best way to trigger recall is by association. Cues provide an associative prompt to facilitate recall.

- Teachers often resist providing context or cues because "it is giving students the answer." Providing a cue (*starts with* S) did not give you the answer. There are about 20 towns in Illinois and New Mexico that start with *S*. If *Springfield* and/or *Santa Fe* popped out, the information had to be in your memory, and the cue facilitated the retrieval. If you didn't know that information, the cue would not have helped.

Task Three

> Recall a conversation that you have been in recently with several people. Was there a point in the conversation that you had a question or wanted to ask for additional information, but it would have been rude to interrupt at that time? By the time you could interject with your comment or question, you forgot what you wanted to say. What did you do to retrieve your comment?

Most people retrace what was being said. By recreating the situation, the association works to re-trigger the question or comment. We might also have to stop the conversation momentarily while we engage in that retracking so something else doesn't distract us, or at least tune it out. There! You remember, ask, and feel great about recalling it. Somehow you decide you haven't started down the path to senility yet. Your efforts to remember were rewarded, and you have reinforced a compensatory strategy for retrieval.

Task Three Lessons

- You knew how to retrieve information and could apply that strategy effectively within the situation.

- Constant attention was counterproductive to the retrieval process. You required some "quiet time" or tuned out of the conversation to collect your thoughts. You were more productive and effective by allowing yourself some internal processing time.

- Associative context was the best strategy to recall the forgotten language information.

Task Four

Recall a situation in which your thinking process was timed. It might have been a standardized test, such as *ACT, SAT, GRE,* or *CCC.* If you have a really good memory, you might recall timed math fact tests, reading comprehension tests, spelling tests, or *Iowa Tests of Basic Skills* from your childhood school days.

Are those pleasant memories? Did the timing give you confidence and make you feel good about your answers? Or did you walk out frustrated that you had rushed, not gotten to some questions, or experienced anxiety that you might not finish, even though you did?

What do timed tests tell us? Some educational research experts advocate them for spelling, math facts, etc., because they provide insight to *automaticity in learning,* i.e., information has become ingrained to the point of it being automatic and not requiring lots of thought. Is that a teacher's goal? And while children are learning it, do we want them rushing through or going slowly to make sure their work is accurate?

Most standardized tests are timed merely for convenience of administration. Designers determine what appears to be a reasonable timeframe to assess the targeted knowledge. Should learning in a classroom be about convenience for the teacher?

For children who have language processing deficits, timed tests accomplish very little. Does the teacher want to know if students know the information or if they can do the task fast? The two questions don't go together when information is being learned. For a student with a language processing disorder, the answer is *I can't do it fast, so don't frustrate me with that experience.* Find out if the student knows it by taking the pressure off and encouraging the child to use a *good* effort rather than a *fast* effort.

Task Four Lessons

- Timed learning tasks during the developmental years add more pressure and compromise careful effort for children with processing problems.

- Timed tests send a message that thinking should be automatic and fast as opposed to careful and deliberate.

- Timed tasks do not necessarily make children feel good about their performance or confident about their answers.

These tasks should have served to illustrate that a percentage of processing problems are the result of difficulties in retrieval: accessing information already acquired accurately and efficiently. Remediation in the area of word retrieval requires sorting out which cues work well for a student and teaching her how to access information she has stored.

A hierarchy for teaching word retrieval is included in the *Language Processing Kit* (Richard & Hanner, 1995). The initial goal is always accuracy. There is no point in being fast but inaccurate! Accuracy should always be addressed first, without time demands. Efficiency or speed in processing is secondary.

A child with word retrieval problems needs to learn how to carefully organize information as it is encoded and stored to facilitate later retrieval. If language information is not "put in" well, it won't "come out" effectively.

A story I use to illustrate this is to imagine a teenager's bedroom. Her organization of clothing as well as other things can be rather haphazard. Imagine it is Friday night during the winter, and the student is going to the high school basketball game. Her ride is waiting out front. She HAS to wear a certain sweater, but she can't find it. She and her parents both know the sweater is somewhere in the house, but the search is on as to where. The girl might check the pile of clothes under her bed, on the closet floor, in the corner, or downstairs in the laundry. Mom might check drawers, hangers, and shelves. Dad might check with a younger sister or various piles in other closets. Efficiency has definitely been compromised! So far, accuracy is also coming up short. The parents might eventually decide the search is over, saying, "Wear something else or don't go." Their daughter leaves in a huff, and the parents are not in a pleasant mood.

When the daughter returns, her parents explain that there will not be a repeat performance next Friday night. Her room must be cleaned up and organized. If the parents completed that task while their daughter was at the game, it would not help her efficiency or accuracy next week. She must clean up and organize in a way that makes sense to her so she can find her sweater and other items more efficiently and accurately in the future. It might be easier for the parents to do it for their daughter, but in the long run, that wouldn't help her be more accurate or efficient in finding her belongings herself.

The moral of the story: word retrieval therapy has to use the child's organization system, or it won't help. A teacher supplying an answer is as though one of the parents found the sweater, not the daughter, and it won't help next time. To give up and take another sweater improves efficiency, but it's the wrong sweater, so accuracy is still compromised. Therapy must help the student figure out which associative retrieval strategies work for her and then take the time to make sure she carefully organizes information (encodes) as it goes into the room (long term memory) so it can be retrieved accurately and efficiently.

Then a teacher or parent can provide associative cues to facilitate retrieval. Parents can say, "Remember, you folded your sweaters and put them on the closet shelf." A teacher can remind a student of other information surrounding the material being sought, which should trigger the retrieval by association. Once the student experiences success in retrieval, he can learn to ask himself the same questions the teacher asked him. This behavior facilitates self-retrieval strategies, exactly as you did for yourself in the four tasks earlier.

The goal in working with word retrieval is always **accuracy first**. Help the student with language processing deficits learn to persevere and dig in long term memory until she finds the desired information. Teach the student to request cues or hints to facilitate the process rather than give up. Once accuracy has been achieved, address the speed of retrieval or the efficiency.

The neurological Processing Continuum Model strongly supports a positive improvement in word retrieval if it is directly targeted with students who have processing deficits. The student with retrieval problems has to learn how to organize language information by attaching increased levels of associative meaning to the stimulus. That's exactly what language processing is: attaching increased levels of meaning to auditory input to achieve more complex cognitive interaction with the content. It is accomplished by spending more time with information to add more connections or associative attachments to it.

The neurology of learning indicates that learning changes the brain. When the brain receives a stimulus, it starts a neurological processing chain. The stimulus is sorted and processed at several levels of meaning or complexity along the continuum. Each level adds formation of memory potential. Learning means growing more synaptic connections between information and not losing connections already in place. The brain modifies itself based on the type and amount of use. Processing is achieved when the brain makes connections, which equals learning.

The neurological Processing Continuum Model not only explains the rationale for providing compensatory strategies, but it also makes a strong case for remediating specific areas of deficits. That will be addressed later in this chapter, but the model reinforces the importance of implementing strategies to overcome language processing disorders. Compensatory strategies put modifications in place that allow a child with language processing problems to cope, re-learn, and begin to resolve the difficulties present. It also alleviates frustration!

Compensatory Strategies

The neurological Processing Continuum Model supports the fact that we aren't yet able to "fix" or repair brains that function differently. However, by implementing modification strategies to assist or compensate for deficits, the brain can assume the required language processing functions in a limited way. The compensatory strategies require a shared responsibility between teachers/parents and the student with a language processing deficit. Some of the modifications must be initiated by a teacher or an adult to facilitate success in an academic setting. Other modifications require a concerted effort on the part of the student with language processing deficits to implement and use strategies allowed or introduced by adults.

Teachers need to understand the importance of providing modifications for a student with language processing deficits. Such a student has normal intelligence and generally age-commensurate language development but struggles to integrate and use that language knowledge in more complex academic tasks.

Teachers must keep in mind that language processing deficits are not behavioral or manipulative avoidance. The child isn't choosing to perform poorly or struggle to respond. Processing deficits are caused by neurological glitches in the secondary and tertiary areas of the brain. To presume that a deaf child can hear if he just tries hard enough is a fair analogy for the teacher who resists compensatory strategies. The problem is legitimate and should be approached like any other neurological deficit.

Teacher Compensatory Strategies

Teachers need to use specific strategies to facilitate success for students with language processing disorders. A list of ten suggestions is provided at the top of page 149, followed by a short explanation of each one.

Teacher Compensatory Strategies for LPD

1. Introduce information using a multimodality approach for sensory stimulation.
2. Supplement auditory information with visual materials.
3. Introduce new material in a context-rich, associative environment.
4. Provide cues, prompts, or hints to help focus students and facilitate retrieval.
5. Allow "thinking time"; monitor external pressure when latencies occur.
6. Limit timed activities or performance tasks; allow extra time.
7. Shorten length of assignments to focus on accuracy rather than efficiency.
8. Vary the types of responses expected on exams and in class discussions.
9. Refresh stimuli with repetition, rephrasing, and expansion clarifications.
10. Teach with stories and examples to associate main points of auditory information.

1. Introduce information using a multimodality approach.

A stimulus will be stronger if it is experienced in multiple areas of the brain. Presenting information using visual, tactile, motor, auditory, and other sensory channels enhances the strength of the signal and increases areas of the brain stimulated and actively processing the stimulus.

2. Supplement auditory information with visual materials.

The auditory signal is very brief and dissipates immediately. If the student couldn't get it processed quickly, the stimulus is gone. Back up auditory information with a more permanent visual record when possible. Write key words, assignments, or definitions on the board or an overhead projector. Post project explanations, exam dates, and important information to be read or copied. Check notes to make sure key information was copied down as it was presented verbally in class.

3. Introduce new material in a context-rich, associative environment.

Remember that retrieval is enhanced by the number and amount of other material attached to new information. Introduce new information in contextual units surrounded by pertinent, associated material that should facilitate recall. Review previous information related to new content. Avoid introducing disjointed facts that the student must organize.

4. Provide cues, prompts, or hints to help focus students.

Provide additional information, descriptions, the first sound, associated features, other items in the category, etc., to help a student focus on the pertinent area for retrieval. Think of strategies that work for you to retrieve information, and teach them to the student.

5. Allow "thinking time"; monitor external pressure when latencies occur.

Students with processing problems need more time to make neurological connections. The normal latency between a question and response is two-to-four seconds. That is not enough time for a student with language processing problems to attach meaning to the questions and activate retrieval strategies to find the information. If the teacher looks impatient or other students are waving their arms frantically to be called on, the student who needs longer will become uncomfortable and give up. A good strategy is to ask a question and provide the whole class with "thinking time." No hands go up until you give a signal. Then the student who needs more time isn't the only one using extra assimilation time. It might also help other students not to be so impulsive!

6. Limit timed activities or performance tasks.

Consider very carefully timed performance tasks in a classroom. The message sent is to work quickly as opposed to accurately. It also further stresses an already overworked neurological system for the student with language processing problems. Timed performance could be optional, but accuracy must be the focus. It might also be possible to tell students to do as many as possible in the time, but double points come off for any wrong. Teachers should promote accurate, high quality work rather than rushed work.

7. Shorten length of assignments to focus on accuracy.

The student with language processing deficits is likely to require extra time on exams or assignments to accommodate his slower latency in retrieving and organizing information. A teacher should make arrangements so that this does penalize the student in any way, including with peers.

8. Vary the types of responses expected on exams/class discussions.

Teachers should use a variety of types of questions and response modes required of students. Some teachers won't rephrase or explain questions a student doesn't understand. It's almost like the student is supposed to read the teacher's mind! The purpose of assignments and exams is to know what the student has learned. Accommodate different learning styles, and be sure associative context is provided for questions.

Research has shown that the difficulty of a response affects a student's performance. Over half of the questions asked (57%) in the typical school setting require total recall. Approximately 30% require higher-level language processing skills of conjecture, explanation, and evaluation. Fewer than 14% are recognition questions, yet the format of most of the standardized national assessment exams (*SAT, ACT, GRE*) is multiple-choice recognition questions. Educators can still discern if students know information from multiple-choice questions. Providing an associative context isn't providing the answer; the student still has to have learned the content.

9. Refresh stimuli with repetition, rephrasing, and expansion clarifications.

Just when a student with language processing problems might begin attaching meaning to auditory input from the teacher, his train of thought might be derailed by a distraction. He will have to give up or rely on others to catch up unless the teacher is in the habit of paraphrasing, repeating, or expanding with explanations. Every student can benefit from hearing something twice; it serves as a check on the processing students have completed so far.

10. Teach with stories and examples to associate main points.

Relevant information is usually easier to process because a student can use personal experiences to help process the material. New material is more challenging. Teachers who share stories and examples provide an associative context for information that helps students remember verbal information. Many times a person remembers the story or personal anecdote associated with a main point, which then leads to recall of the more specific content information.

Student Compensatory Strategies

Students with language processing disorders also need to be taught strategies they can use to facilitate their classroom success. A list of ten suggestions is listed at the top of page 152, followed by a short explanation of each one.

Student Compensatory Strategies for Language Processing Disorders

1. Request additional time when you need it.

2. Request cues, prompts, and associative information.

3. Ask specific questions rather than generic questions.

4. Apply strategies taught in therapy that work to facilitate retrieval.

5. State what you do know, then the source of confusion.

6. Tape record lectures to provide repetition or a more permanent record.

7. Use rehearsal, paraphrasing, and writing key words to keep processing on track.

8. Be an active learner rather than a passive learner.

9. Be patient; take your time, and don't give up or become frustrated.

10. Seek out study buddies to check information.

1. Request additional time when you need it.

Teachers might not think to offer extra time, but they might not be opposed to it. If you need extra time to achieve a more accurate representation of what you think you know, politely request it from your teachers. Don't abuse it or make it a habit, but use it when it can make a positive difference in your performance.

2. Request cues, prompts, and associative information.

When you know an answer but can't seem to retrieve it, don't give up and respond with "I don't know." Ask the teacher if she could give you the first letter or some other cue that works well to focus your recall process. This strategy lets the teacher know that you are interested and trying to remember the answer.

3. Ask specific questions rather than generic questions.

When you're confused, don't say "I don't get it" or "Can you say that all again?" Teachers are likely to interpret minimal effort on your part in those comments. Instead, ask more specific questions that let the teacher know what part is confusing you or at what point your comprehension became cloudy.

4. Use retrieval strategies taught in therapy that work for you.

Self-cuing is always the goal for a student with retrieval problems. Once a speech-language pathologist has modeled and taught you strategies that facilitate word recall, try to initiate those techniques by yourself.

5. State what you *do* know.

Paraphrasing or repeating information back to a teacher is a good check on comprehension. It also lets the teacher know what portions of content you processed accurately and where confusion may be entering. Restating the information received gives the teacher concrete feedback and provides you with additional processing time.

6. Tape record lectures to provide repetition or a more permanent record.

In classes where verbal presentation is rapid and accompanied by little visual or other supportive stimuli, tape record the teacher to provide a permanent record of content from which you can take notes later. Replaying the tape also allows you to hear the explanation again, which should help your processing.

7. Use rehearsal, paraphrasing, and writing key words to keep on track.

Many people jot notes, mumble to themselves, or rephrase information to force themselves to pay attention, record or refresh pertinent facts, and provide a check on comprehension.

8. Be an active learner rather than a passive learner.

Pay attention, focus, watch visual cues carefully, anticipate content, and enter discussions. Don't be afraid to ask questions or seek clarification. An active learner is often rewarded for having a positive attitude with a more patient and interested teacher.

9. Be patient; take your time, and don't give up or become frustrated.

Your neurological system is working at full speed, despite how it compares to other students' systems. The way your system will improve is to keep using it and grooving those synaptic connections. Don't give up, become emotional, or add more pressure. Impatience will only cause further failure in your language processing system.

10. Seek out study buddies to check information.

Teachers sometimes have their hands full and are overscheduled. A way to reassure yourself and make sure your processing efforts are accurate is to access other students in the class. Studying together or quizzing each other gives you an opportunity to expand and strengthen your learning without relying on your teachers' time and efforts.

Specific Skills Intervention

I'm sorry to say there is no magic cookbook for language processing remediation. Some speech-language pathologists have confidently started on page one of therapy programs and decided that when the child finishes the program or book, processing will have been remediated. Despite their best efforts, that is not the way to approach language processing intervention. That method is still behavioral, based on available therapy resources. It is still hit and miss, based on what language tasks are covered in the therapy resource.

Early in this book, the neurological Processing Continuum Model was introduced to explain the processing continuum. This model is used to guide assessment decisions to avoid hit and miss diagnosis. The same theoretical model must also be used to guide intervention goals.

Intervention can only be as effective as your diagnosis. If assessment instruments are designed as complex tasks with multiple variables in each subtest, how do you know which discrete language skills are a problem? Assessment should follow the neurological hierarchy of gradually attaching more meaning to language. Each layer must be peeled away to determine if a language skill is intact or deficient.

The case examples presented in Chapter 5 stressed that part of diagnosis is determining what works as well as what is deficient in language areas. If a speech-language pathologist or teacher doesn't know if a student has language delays, how can we determine whether the problem is language foundation skills or processing? If memory is significantly impaired, a teacher must compensate to insure that information is received to be processed rather than lost before the child can begin attaching meaning to it.

Part of successful language processing therapy is knowing how to present information to remediate the problem rather than frustrate the child. The goal is not to drill deficits but to provide language processing experiences in which the child can be successful. Each time a student accurately processes auditory information, stronger synaptic connections are being forged for the next time. It is important not to try to make the blind child "see," à la drilling deficits. The purpose is to get the information to the child in a way that she can attach meaning to what she hears.

The speech-language pathologist must use knowledge of language to determine an appropriate order for language processing goals. The goals are the same as always. The materials can be the same. The difference is the hierarchical order in which the language goals are addressed.

Guidelines for Language Processing Therapy

The following list provides general guidelines to follow when designing language processing remediation.

- **Use results from the *Language Processing Test (LPT)* or a similar assessment to determine the level of language processing development.** This is a critical, important step. Assessment must sample discrete language skills to evaluate varying levels of language complexity. The level of competence and level of breakdown or difficulty are both important. The clinician must know what types of language processing tasks a child can competently do and which ones are in deficit.

- **Begin at the earliest level at which difficulty was encountered, regardless of whether or not higher level skills were intact.** I have seen students struggle to complete the Association and Categorization subtests on the *LPT,* but sail through Similarity and Difference. On Attributes, they provide one or two low-level features per item. Usually they've been in therapy and someone targeted Similarity and Difference without building language processing skills around the task. A splinter skill has been trained, but the child can't apply or use it because other adjunct language areas have not been addressed.

- **Begin at the first level of difficulty, and solidify that language processing skill before progressing to the next one.** Attributes is telling you that the child is not able to attach complex levels of meaning independently. If the child simply had a weakness at the early levels and the next levels are intact, then you progress quickly, but you take the time to fill in the holes!

- **Use the entire second functional unit to approach intervention, gradually moving toward auditory input only.** Always introduce language processing therapy materials with stimuli to all three lobes (occipital, parietal, and temporal) to facilitate successful processing. Once the cognitive language task is being handled, remove physical (parietal) input and retain visual and auditory stimuli. Once the task is being successfully handled in two-modality presentation, remove visual cues (occipital), and see if the student can successfully process the task from auditory stimuli only (temporal). That's always the goal, but that isn't where teaching starts; it works gradually to groove in the neurological connections to process language successfully, using strengths to overcome weaknesses.

The *Language Processing Kit* follows this progression. Goals begin with objects to manipulate, pictures, and auditory stimuli. The second group of tasks use visual stimuli of pictures to accompany the verbal processing tasks. The third group is verbal input only, with a gradual increase in efficiency through time demands. Other therapy materials can certainly be used in place of the kit. The important point to remember is to use multisensory stimulation to facilitate neurological development of processing skills.

- **Order goals/deficit areas into language levels of cognitive complexity.** Assessment results should identify language tasks that are problematic or discrepant from expected performance. All the goals may be legitimate goals, but they shouldn't all be worked on at the same time. Examine the language goals and determine what language skills are prerequisite to complete the language task in deficit. Then impose a sequence in which to address the goals that gradually build up to the most complex. Think about the model from articulation: sound in isolation, syllable, word, phrase, sentence, then conversation. Language skills must also build up gradually in neurological demand.

- **Start with discrete language skills and work into more integrated language skills.** Speech-language pathologists sometimes argue that working on specific language skills isn't functional and won't translate into academic learning success. The neurological model helps refute this argument. A child who wants to learn to play basketball can't just be thrown into a competitive game. He must work to develop the discrete skills of dribbling, shooting, running and dribbling, running and shooting, etc. The isolated skills will build the foundation to carryover into functional tasks. Discrete language skills should never be the only skills addressed; functional application must also be incorporated into therapy.

- **Think hierarchy; impose levels of language complexity on your goals.** All language tasks are not the same in terms of cognitive complexity. Some language tasks require multiple, other language skills to already be in place. Avoid random decisions about the order in which to approach language processing goals. For example, a goal to work on *Wh-* questions is a good language processing goal, but are all *Wh-* questions equal in regard to language complexity and demand? Does answering a *who* or *what* question require the same level of language skill as a *where* or *when*, or as a *how* or *why* question? There is an obvious hierarchy within *Wh-* questions that needs to be considered when implementing that goal.

- **Use the neuropsychological model to guide goals through the secondary zone, to the tertiary zone, to the frontal lobe/third functional unit for output.** Secondary zone discrete language skills were preliminarily spelled out in the *Language Processing Test* areas (naming, labeling, association, categorization, etc.). The hierarchical order follows normal language development (i.e., nouns, verbs, attribute features, etc.). Tertiary zone skills become more integrated language tasks, such as reading comprehension, and work into frontal lobe integration for organization, problem solving, reasoning, etc. Language processing goals should progress across the neurological model but maintain a hierarchical order. For example, it would not be appropriate to work on developing functions in the secondary zone while working on problem solving and reasoning at a tertiary/frontal lobe level.

- **Impose cues/prompts into all language processing remediation.** Word retrieval strategies are global and should always be incorporated as necessary into any language processing therapy. Anytime a student is having difficulty retrieving or organizing information, provide cues and prompts to facilitate the response being generated by the student.

- **Work in conjunction with the compensatory strategies and adjunct areas (memory, cueing, latency, etc.)** Language processing effectiveness will be directly influenced by adjunct areas of strength and weakness. If central auditory processing weaknesses are also present, those strategies must be incorporated into language processing therapy. If short term memory is a problem, supplemental visuals or redundant auditory signals must be provided to facilitate accurate reception of the stimulus before it can be processed.

- **Examine therapy resource materials carefully. Use clinical judgment to determine the order in which sections or materials in the book are introduced.** It isn't necessary to reinvent the wheel. Many excellent therapy resources for language processing therapy are available. The problem is there is no theoretical model within their structure. The materials on page 1 are not necessarily easier than materials on page 31 or 101. No analysis has been conducted to determine cognitive complexity or language demand in various tasks. That is your task as the professional.

Discrete Hierarchy

Imposing a hierarchy on language goals can be an intimidating task. It will become easier with practice and there is no absolute right or wrong, but it is important to understand the basic concept of the hierarchy of cognitive complexity.

The goal in language processing assessment is to sample discrete skills at different levels. We could illustrate that as a high, narrow tower, with each discrete skill of subtest areas representing a floor in the tower. We would start on the ground floor with labeling and work up to multiple meanings (see diagram on next page).

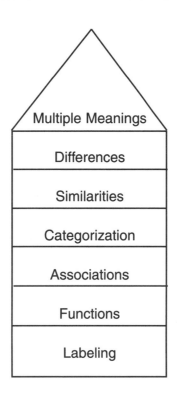

The goal in language processing remediation is to strengthen each floor with additional language skills to broaden into a wide strong foundation. Then as new language skills are added, they are built on a strong base. We don't want to keep adding additional floors on top without expanding the foundation. Otherwise the tower will topple over, resulting in academic failure.

You should rarely be working two levels from the above language tower at once because they represent discrete hierarchical levels of cognitive complexity. That would be like teaching a piano student how to play the scales while also working on a concerto. One skill serves as the foundation or building block to scaffold toward the next one. It is not efficient to work a foundation skill while working a more complex applied skill. In fact, it diminishes focused effort on the basic skill and frustrates both the teacher and the student!

As mentioned in discussing assessment, there is nothing magic about this hierarchy other than it represents a hierarchy of skill development by age. We could add higher-level skills on top of multiple meanings to project into adolescent language processing skills with skills like idioms and analogies. Older students with language processing deficits struggle with skills in figurative language, humor, ambiguous language, and inferences. All of these discrete skills are appropriate language processing goals.

But instead, let's try generating some language goals to broaden out the foundation and determine when they should be addressed. Think about the following discrete language goals and determine where you would add them to the hierarchical tower.

Basic concepts (*above, below, few, many, around, between, whole, half, first, second, pair, next to,* etc.)

Antonyms

Synonyms

Where did you put basic concept development? You could make an argument that the concepts should actually spread over several levels, but what's the earliest level you should introduce them? In other words, what level does a child have to minimally attain in language processing to be ready to handle concepts?

Labeling is very concrete object naming. Functions is still very concrete, based in action verbs built upon knowledge of the object involved. Association is experiential; I can see and experience that these two objects go together. Categorization is really the first level of language processing that becomes abstract and isn't always easily demonstrated or shown. By the time I get to similarities and differences, I need those concepts to explain the comparative and contrastive features, so concepts should be introduced before similarities.

How concrete are concepts? Can you show me an *above*? Can you tell me a constant number that represents *few*? All concepts are in relationship to something else, so there is a certain level of abstraction required to process these terms. Therefore, I would put concepts at the level of categorization in terms of the cognitive level of demand.

How about antonyms and synonyms? If you go through the same process as above, you would probably reach a similar conclusion. That type of discrete language processing skill is required to successfully handle similarities and differences, but it introduces abstraction at least at the level of categorization. So if we redrew our tower with those goals added, they should be addressed before initiating similarities (see page 160). These are examples of additional language goals to broaden the foundation at the various levels of language processing and strengthen the language base before moving into more complex language tasks.

So language processing remediation involves addressing language goals that scaffold into higher-level, more complex demands throughout the academic years. By approximately age five, a child's foundation of general semantic, syntax, phonology, morphology, and pragmatic aspects of language has been established. Throughout the school years, teachers build on those basic language skills and require increased cognitive complexity in language tasks. Language processing continues throughout life! Whenever we acquire new information and add it onto previous knowledge, we are processing language at a deeper, more complex level.

Applied Language Processing Skills

The functional application of discrete language skills should also be addressed in language processing therapy. Once a discrete skill has developed, therapy should address functional generalization of the skill.

For example, once the concept and vocabulary of antonyms has been mastered, incorporate application of that language processing task into functional activities. Take an "opposite walk" and find as many opposite pairs as possible in real life. Challenge the child to do the opposite of what you do. Play guessing games that incorporate opposites.

It's also important to think across the processing continuum and all language areas. As you initiate remediation in writing, reasoning, pragmatics, and problem solving, impose a hierarchy on the goals and build the language processing skills to approach the tasks. Don't just work on a language area because it is in deficit. Determine if a student is ready to work on it and has the prerequisite language skills in place to approach that task successfully.

An example might be the area of problem solving. This goal area is frequently addressed for children with language processing deficits. It is important to approach problem solving in a hierarchy rather than just throwing out situations for the child to deal with. Work on one-dimensional problem solving by building discrete skills, such as identifying the problem, generating possible solutions, evaluating solutions, avoiding problems, etc. Approach each of these one at a time, not all at once. Once the student has mastered these with a discrete focus, you can approach the multidimensional problem-solving task of presenting a situation for the child to work through. The other discrete skills have to be developed before the child can apply them independently in functional situations.

A variety of therapy resource programs are listed below. Many of these materials provide excellent global exercises for addressing goals within language processing. There are also many workbooks available to drill discrete skills, such as similarities and differences, idioms, concepts, vocabulary, etc. The challenge for the clinician is to determine how and when to use them!

Materials for Language Processing Skills Training

Follow Me! by Grace Frank, LinguiSystems, Inc., East Moline, IL.

The Listening Kit, The Word Kit, The TOPS Kit, and *The Language Processing Kit,* all available from LinguiSystems, Inc., East Moline, IL.

The *HELP* books (*Handbook of Exercises for Language Processing*) by Andrea Lazzari and Patricia Peters, LinguiSystems, Inc., East Moline, IL.

Vocabulary Maps by Jean Hamersky, Thinking Publications, Eau Claire, WI.

Figurative Language by Kathleen Gorman-Gard, Thinking Publications, Eau Claire, WI.

Language Exercises for Auditory Processing (LEAP) by Larry Mattes and Patty Schuchardt, Academic Communication Associates, Oceanside, CA.

There are also a variety of materials to assist with addressing word retrieval deficits. A few examples are listed below.

Word Finding Intervention Program by Diane German, Pro-Ed, Austin, TX.

HELP for Word Finding by Andrea Lazzari and Patricia Peters, LinguiSystems, Inc., East Moline, IL.

WordBURST by Gina Williamson and Susan Shields, LinguiSystems, Inc., East Moline, IL.

Word Retrieval Exercises for Adolescents and Adults, Academic Communication Associates, Oceanside, CA.

Summary Comments

I hope the pieces of the processing puzzle are beginning to fall into place for you. The neurology discussion you may have avoided or not enjoyed struggling through should (hopefully!) be making sense, and little light bulbs are starting to appear as you read and reread sections of this book.

Common threads should also be becoming apparent. As in central auditory processing disorders, the language processing remediation has two prongs: compensatory techniques and specific skill intervention. The neurological Processing Continuum Model guides decisions all through the continuum for both assessment and intervention. Skills in deficit areas shouldn't be drilled. They should be approached using strengths from other modalities until weaknesses have diminished. Practice and successful learning experiences will build new neurological connections.

And hierarchy must be imposed, just as it is in other communication therapy approaches. Language skills must be evaluated in terms of the cognitive demand and complexity, not targeted because students can't do them well. Evaluate therapy materials logically when choosing resources and activities to address specific goals.

A speech-language pathologist is not a technician. Despite the desire for a ready-to-go therapy plan, cookbook approaches aren't very successful with language training because language is complex. Professionals must use their expertise and knowledge of normal language acquisition to design and implement treatment goals effectively.

Chapter 8: Additional Intervention Ideas

There are additional theoretical approaches to teaching that embrace and reinforce the neurological model of processing outlined in this book. Even within the field of communication disorders, numerous theories, models, and programs offer alternatives to the behavioral models that have dominated therapy for decades. Remediation for processing disorders is not an exact science. There are not definitive *do's* and *don'ts*, yet there are general principles or concepts that should be evident in intervention.

- **One important concept is to think about the whole brain, not just the auditory areas.** If the language sections are in deficit, don't drill what is weak. Compensate and stimulate from other modalities.

- **The second concept is to think in a hierarchy.** Random selection of goals violates sound practice and frustrates everyone involved. Evaluate tasks to determine easy cognitive language demands, and progress to more complex processing tasks.

- **The third concept is to move away from behavioral orientations and begin to incorporate neurological research on learning.** The brain mediates behavior. Every language response serves as an indication of how the brain is functioning. We need to think about stimulation and remediation that is consistent with brain structures and functioning.

- **And finally, explore innovative ideas.** Don't stay in the same rut because that's the way it has always been done. Some old ideas make sense in light of recent research and discoveries about learning. Two theories explained in the following section offer exciting options for processing intervention.

Bloom's Taxonomy

Dr. Benjamin Bloom and his colleagues assembled together in a series of conferences from 1949 to 1953 to design a model composed of educational goals or outcomes in the cognitive area. The idea grew out of a discussion at the 1948 American Psychological Association meeting in which the desire for a common theoretical framework was expressed to facilitate improved communication within the educational and cognitive disciplines. The idea was to provide a guide for teachers as they developed curriculum and learning objectives for students.

The terminology to devise a "taxonomy" was based in the well known biology taxonomy that allowed classification of animals and plants. The professionals wanted to apply the same principle to devise an educational taxonomy with a standard classification for teachers so they could share common ground when discussing curriculum goals and evaluation techniques.

The development of the taxonomy was a monumental undertaking that incorporated the best concepts of the time in regard to teaching and learning practices. The extensive creative process resulted in a book entitled *Taxonomy of Educational Objectives: The Classification of Educational Goals—Handbook 1, Cognitive Domain* with Dr. Benjamin Bloom as the editor. Despite being formulated almost fifty years ago, it continues to provide a comprehensive and substantive model to guide teaching principles.

The thoroughness of the taxonomy is remarkable when you consider the timeframe of its development. Education was founded in behavioral principles of rote learning and continued to ascribe to that paradigm for decades after the 1950s. Yet this group of innovative thinkers postulated a theoretical model that encompassed thinking, feeling, motivation, and cognitive complexity.

The neuropsychological Processing Continuum Model imposes a cognitive hierarchy on the development of processing skills; Bloom's taxonomy does the same. The taxonomy defines a hierarchy of developing cognitive thinking skills in a sequenced order of increased cognitive demand. The language demand in each step of Bloom's taxonomy gradually increases the depth of language processing a child must complete for a stimulus. For this reason, Bloom's taxonomy works very well as an adjunct resource when working on language processing. The chart of thinking skills presented in a hierarchical progression of increased complexity levels is provided on page 165.

When a learning activity is presented, the teacher should move through the hierarchy of cognitive thinking. For a child with a language processing disorder, the distinct levels all qualify as goals to target in remediation.

The concept of the narrow versus a broad base of language processing remediation (see pages 157-160) is extended through the Bloom materials. If you recall the narrow processing chart (page 158), the goal in effective processing therapy is to expand at each floor or level of cognitive language complexity. Bloom advocates the same concept. Each taxonomy level serves as the identifying level of cognitive complexity. Effective teaching expands into other thinking or processing tasks at that level before moving to the next level. Examples of appropriate tasks or goals to expand and solidify the foundation of the Bloom levels are charted on page 166.

Once again, words of caution to practitioners who pick up Bloom's taxonomy and, as with the language processing hierarchy, only work one skill per level and move on. When a child is dismissed as "remediated" after this kind of training, he has only a sample skill at each processing level rather than a solid language foundation to handle a variety of cognitive language tasks at a specified level. Each one of the words on the blocks constitutes another possible language processing goal to expand horizontally rather than vertically on the hierarchy of processing.

Bloom's Taxonomy

Thinking Skill Levels	Descriptions	Goals
Knowledge	The child can recall bits of information.	to learn basic facts and information; to remember information long enough to answer simple questions about it
Comprehension	The child can understand information given, but cannot yet relate it to other material.	to demonstrate knowledge by describing or explaining events in his own words
Application	The child can use what he or she already knows in new situations.	to use previously learned knowledge to solve problems in new situations
Analysis	The child can break a whole into its parts.	to take a situation apart, list the components, and discuss how it was done
Synthesis	The child can put parts together to form a new whole.	to compare the relationships among ideas and situations; to abstract from previous knowledge to form new or creative ideas
Evaluation	The child can state his or her opinions and give reasons.	to state opinions and infer emotions given a situation; to justify answers

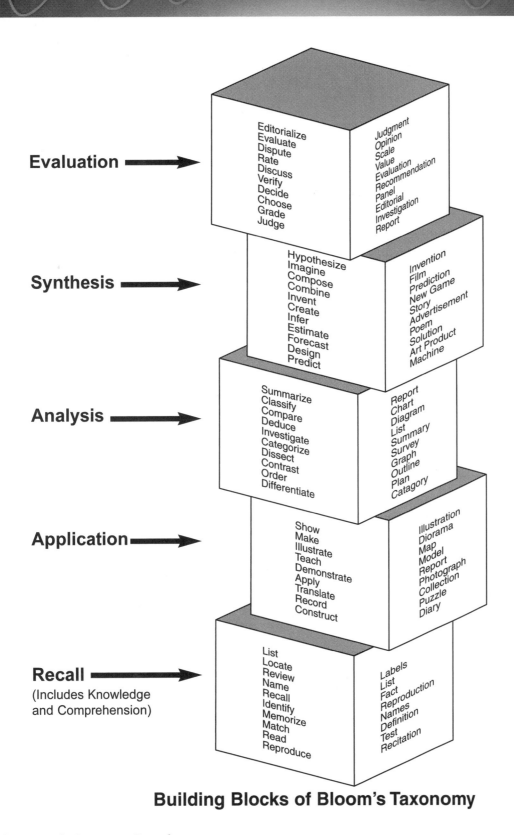

Evaluation ➤

Editorialize
Evaluate
Dispute
Rate
Discuss
Verify
Decide
Choose
Grade
Judge

Judgment
Opinion
Scale
Value
Evaluation
Recommendation
Panel
Editorial
Investigation
Report

Synthesis ➤

Hypothesize
Imagine
Compose
Combine
Invent
Create
Infer
Estimate
Forecast
Design
Predict

Invention
Film
Prediction
New Game
Story
Advertisement
Poem
Solution
Art Product
Machine

Analysis ➤

Summarize
Classify
Compare
Deduce
Investigate
Categorize
Dissect
Contrast
Order
Differentiate

Report
Chart
Diagram
List
Summary
Survey
Graph
Outline
Plan
Catagory

Application ➤

Show
Make
Illustrate
Teach
Demonstrate
Apply
Translate
Record
Construct

Illustration
Diorama
Map
Model
Report
Photograph
Collection
Puzzle
Diary

Recall ➤
(Includes Knowledge
and Comprehension)

List
Locate
Review
Name
Recall
Identify
Memorize
Match
Read
Reproduce

Labels
List
Fact
Reproduction
Names
Definition
Test
Recitation

Building Blocks of Bloom's Taxonomy

The other concept that can be incorporated effectively into Bloom's taxonomy is the idea of hands-on experiences, such as craft projects or simple science experiments. Such activities are not just auditory presentation of information; they involve the whole brain with visual, motor, and sensory stimulation to accompany and clarify the verbal input. In many ways, Bloom and his colleagues were decades ahead of the educational field with their landmark work. The principles advocated in the taxonomy fit right into the push for a paradigm shift to recognition of the brain's role in mediating behavior—or the neuropsychological approach to teaching and language!

Multiple Intelligences

Dr. Howard Gardner was part of a group of researchers at the Harvard Graduate School of Education in 1979. These researchers sought to explore and explain the concept of human potential in cognizance with cognitive development. The study resulted in a 1983 publication called *Frames of Mind*. The unusual aspect, which was met rather frostily by fellow psychologists, was that Dr. Gardner worded his theory not as different talents but as "multiple intelligences."

The reaction from peers was not particularly positive. However, educators were intrigued with the concept and embraced it with increased excitement over the years. Despite the lack of empirical research to substantiate the theory, teachers felt affirmed in their perceptions that students learn differently and present with different aptitudes for various kinds of information.

The theory advocates that human cognitive competence can be described as a set of abilities or skills defined as an "intelligence." Any one person can excel in one or more of these intelligences, but not all humans share the same aptitudes to excel in identical intelligences. To force children in school to learn or excel in linguistic intelligence could be minimizing their other exceptional talents or potential.

Gardner defined an intelligence as an ability to solve problems in a particular venue or to create products that are valued across cultures. Each intelligence has a unique, defined set of core operations. Each intelligence is activated by certain internally or externally presented information, and it has an established symbol system of meaning.

People possess varying degrees of competence in the intelligences, which determines how they learn and what skills they will struggle and excel within. Gardner described five levels of competence as they apply to each intelligence. These levels are described on pages 168-169.

- Pre-beginner   no awareness or interest in the intelligence area

- Beginner   awareness of the basic features or symbolic code system; person's performance would be classified as trial and error; person would not be described as an independent learner in the intelligence area

- Intermediate   can function effectively using the basic skills or symbolic code system; person can learn from personal errors in performance and assist others at a beginning level

- Master   possesses automatic skill in performing within the intelligence area with minimal conscious effort; person is able to teach others the basic code or symbol system of the intelligence

- Expert   demonstrates a professional expertise in performing this intelligence; is able to manipulate the symbolic code system to create new works in the intelligence area

Gardner's initial work defined seven intelligences. He added an eighth about six years ago and continues to explore a ninth. They are defined in the following chart, as well as an example of a person who might be considered an expert in that intelligence area.

Multiple Intelligences		
Intelligences	*Definitions*	*Example Experts*
Linguistic	ability to communicate through language; uses words effectively	T.S. Eliot
Logical-Mathematical	ability to reason mathematically; can use and appreciate abstract relationships	Albert Einstein
Musical	ability to understand rhythm and notes; can create and understand meaning from sounds	Igor Stravinsky
Spatial	ability in visual imagination and recall; can perceive images, transform, and recreate them	Pablo Picasso
Bodily-Kinesthetic	ability to use all or parts of the body in highly skilled way; demonstrates physical grace and agility	Martha Graham Babe Ruth

continued on the next page

Intelligences	Definitions	Example Experts
Interpersonal	ability to sense others' needs; can recognize and distinguish among others' feelings and intentions	Mahatma Gandhi Anne Sullivan
Intrapersonal	ability to deeply understand one's self; can recognize and distinguish among own feelings to build an accurate mental model of self	Sigmund Freud
Naturalist	ability to distinguish among, classify, and use features of the environment	Charles Darwin
Existential	awareness of a spiritual, religious-type faith or energy	Dalai Lama

A person would be evaluated in the various intelligences in regard to her competency in each one. A profile of strengths and weaknesses would emerge, which would assist others in knowing how to teach or approach that person through a modality of competence.

This is the key aspect of the multiple intelligences theory that correlates well with the neuropsychological approach to processing—the concept of strengths and weaknesses in different intelligences. A child with language processing deficits is not likely to have a strength in linguistic intelligence; however, to try to remediate through the linguistic code system further exacerbates the problem. Multiple intelligences training advocates finding other aptitudes that are strengths and using those to approach the weak linguistic area. This premise correlates with using motor, visual, or other types of stimuli to compensate for the weak area. Rather than drill the deficit, put the information in another modality that works better for the student, and use it to help develop the language processing/linguistic area of deficit.

An example from my own experiences might help to clarify. At the time of this situation, I wasn't aware of the multiple intelligences theory, but I certainly experienced the benefits!

Brandon had just finished his freshman year in high school. He was a gifted athlete and had lettered in three sports as a starter on three varsity sports: football, basketball, and baseball. Despite his incredible talent as an athlete, he was virtually unintelligible when he talked. He had significantly impaired oral-motor skills with an apraxic quality similar to severe cerebral palsy. His parents had sent him to a summer six-week residential camp for speech therapy as a last try to improve his intelligibility.

170

Brandon's motivation for speech therapy was not high. He had been in therapy since he was a small boy with minimal success. Therapy had been fairly traditional with minimal success. Motor control and muscle strength continued to be variable, with intelligibility better for single words and short phrases. He wanted to be at a sports camp, not working on speech, but agreed to try one last time. Lucky me, I was assigned to him as a student speech-language pathologist!

I was a ranked tennis player in college and had an appreciation for athletic talent, a strength in the bodily-kinesthetic intelligence. Brandon shared that intelligence with an intensity that matched mine. I decided the way to approach his weak oral-motor area was through the general body-kinesthetic strength.

We conducted our therapy sessions in the gymnasium. Brandon would perform isometric exercises of pushing against a wall, climbing a rope, push-ups, pull-ups, and weight lifting. On each thrust, he produced a syllable. The isometric tension overflowed to his oral cavity to accomplish increased muscle tone and strength, resulting in improved articulation clarity!

Brandon could hear the difference and was pleasantly surprised. He shared that he had declined interviews with any reporters because of how he sounded. He really wanted to answer some of their questions, but he was afraid they would think he was retarded or slow because of his speech. We made a deal that every time he worked out, he had to pop the words and syllables we were targeting that day. He could work out as often as he wanted in the gym, but vocalization had to accompany the isometric weight workouts.

The change was incredible. Brandon finally felt he was in control and could make a difference in the sound of his speech. Instead of feeling like a failure in speech therapy, he felt successful. Working through a different intelligence dramatically improved his linguistic weakness.

The main advantage of a multiple intelligences approach is that teachers present stimuli in different ways across many sensory aptitudes rather than only verbal language input. Students who struggle to process information presented in a verbal modality might make sense of it in a motor or musical modality. The multidimensional approach to learning fosters creative thinking. The students can also experience success and approach tasks with more confidence.

There are a variety of materials that have been published in the last fifteen years approaching teaching and therapy through multiple intelligences. The resources are available to incorporate multimodality teaching through strengths to compensate and remediate the weaknesses.

Sample Diagnostic Report

A question I am often asked is how to explain processing deficits in a report and how all the information fits together. Rather than try to tell you, I have provided a diagnostic report from a case study conducted several years ago. It is intended to demonstrate a sample evaluation format. It also helps illustrate how to probe within subtest areas for information that guides evaluation results. I hope this example will show how it all comes together!

DIAGNOSTIC EVALUATION REPORT

Name: Clifton ____

Referral Information

Clifton ____, age 7 years, was evaluated at the request of the Director of Special Education. Cliff completed regular kindergarten during the previous school year and will be enrolled in first grade this fall. Previous special services have included speech-language, physical, and occupational therapy, but end-of-the-year evaluations suggested no need for continuation of special services. Concerns prompting the independent evaluation were in regard to remaining speech-language deficits that could impact academic performance. Cliff was brought for the evaluation by his mother.

Formal Evaluation Results

The *Peabody Picture Vocabulary Test-Revised, Form M,* was administered to attain an estimated age equivalency for receptive comprehension of single words. Cliff received a raw score of 100, which converted to an age equivalency of 9 years, 1 month; a percentile rank of 92; and standard score of 121. Performance was interpreted by standardization to be a "moderately high score."

Results indicated that Cliff's core lexicon was well developed for comprehension of pictured semantic vocabulary. This language foundation should serve as the basis for other language abilities.

The *Language Processing Test* was administered to evaluate Cliff's ability to attach meaning to verbally presented language in an increased hierarchy of cognitive complexity. Results were as follows on the next page:

Language Processing Test

Subtest	Raw Score	Age Equivalent	Percentile	Standard Score
Labeling	12	NA (pretest)		
Functions	12	NA (pretest)		
Association	6	below norms	6	78*
Categorization	10	6-8	41	98
Similarities	7	7-6	54	102
Differences	7	7-7	58	105
Multiple Mean.	7	7-9	67	108
Attributes	20	5-9	11	84*
TOTAL TEST	57	6-7	26	91

* More than one standard deviation below the mean (85)

Results indicate overall ability to attach meaning to auditorily presented stimuli to be commensurate with age expectations. However, splintering and inconsistencies within subtests were apparent, particularly in the Association and Attributes subtests. Cliff's difficulty in Association represents a discrepancy in the development of early language skills for processing language stimuli, which could impact later development of more complex processing abilities.

The Attributes subtest revealed a significant discrepancy in Cliff's processing on focused/structured tasks versus unstructured tasks. All previous subtests entailed a very discrete, isolated language task with one variable involved. The Attributes subtest evaluated Cliff's ability to process language without a specific focus or variable being identified for him. His responses consistently addressed early, shallow levels of processing (providing function and components of presented items) with only three additional attributes spontaneously generated of a more complex nature across all twelve stimulus items. Cliff's performance suggests that he relies on visual, immediate information and does not independently complete more abstract interpretation of information without prompts or focus being provided.

The *Test of Word Finding* was administered to evaluate Cliff's ability to retrieve learned information quickly and accurately. Performance summary on this instrument was as follows:

Test of Word Finding

Based on Age		Based on Grade	
Total Raw Score	71	Total Raw Score	71
Standard Score	112	Standard Score	120
Percentile Rank	80	Percentile Rank	91

Word Finding Profile: Fast and Accurate
Percent of comprehension: 90% or above

Cliff's performance indicates adequate ability to effectively and efficiently retrieve single words. His comprehension was 100% for errors, confirming receptive knowledge for items named inaccurately. Cliff's organized retrieval for more complex language information was difficult, as explained later in results for the *Test of Problem Solving*.

Assessing Children's Language Comprehension was administered to evaluate Cliff's auditory memory for meaningful stimuli in the presence of visual context. The instrument established a core group of vocabulary items which were then combined to assess memory length and complexity with two, three, and four critical elements. Results were as follows:

Assessing Children's Language Comprehension

Test Vocabulary	100% correct
Two Critical Elements	100% correct
Three Critical Elements	100% correct
Four Critical Elements	100% correct

The Auditory Sequential Memory subtest from the *Illinois Test of Psycholinguistic Abilities* was administered to evaluate sequential auditory memory for nonmeaningful stimuli. A series of numbers was verbally presented for Cliff to retain and repeat. His performance resulted in a raw score of 26, an age equivalency of 7.2, and a standard score of 36.

Results indicated that Cliff's short term memory for both related and unrelated material was commensurate with age expectations. Inadequate short term working memory did not appear to be a factor in his language performance deficits.

Assessing Semantic Skills through Everyday Themes (ASSET) was administered to evaluate Cliff's receptive and expressive semantic language knowledge using pictured everyday life situations. Results were as follows:

Assessing Semantic Skills Through Everyday Themes

Subtest	Raw Score	Age Equivalent	Percentile	Standard Score
Receptive				
ID Labels	14	8.8	79	113
ID Categories	12	5.11	32	96
ID Attributes	10	5.8	24	91
ID Functions	14	10.6	97	124
ID Definitions	12	7.6	54	104
Receptive Total	**62**	**7.9**	**65**	**107**
Expressive				
State Labels	11	7.8	61	106
State Categories	8	6.9	38	98
State Attributes	10	7.3	48	102
State Functions	8	5.4	20	87
State Definitions	3	4.7	9	78*
Expressive Total	**40**	**6.5**	**33**	**93**
Total Test	**102**	**6.9**	**42**	**99**

* More than one standard deviation below the mean (85)

Cliff's total test performance was within standardization expectations for his age range. However, splintering was again present when examining subtest results. The highest standard score (124) to lowest standard score (78) represented a 46 point difference in language performance. In general, expressive standard scores were lower than receptive language scores. These two patterns suggest significant inconsistencies across Cliff's language abilities.

The *Test of Problem Solving* was administered to evaluate Cliff's ability to integrate verbal language information with pictured situational stimuli to then formulate an expressive response. Results were the following:

Test of Problem Solving

Subtest	Raw Score	Age Equivalent	Percentile	Standard Score
Explaining Inferences	10	5.10	29	47
Determining Causes	8	3.9	18	45
Negative Why Questions	9	5.11	21	46
Determining Solutions	5	4.6	8	42*
Avoiding Problems	4	4.11	7	43*
Total Test	**36**	**4.11**	**8**	**43***

* More than one standard deviation below the mean (45)

Cliff's performance on this assessment instrument was minimal when compared to other evaluation results. Cliff's ability to expressively explain an organized reasoning process was, at best, borderline on three subtests and below expectations on two subtests and the composite test score. Cliff was very dependent on the visual illustrations to derive a response, and he was not able to demonstrate independent abstract reasoning and problem solving. He often missed the main point of questions and responded to an obscure aspect that was not pertinent to the issue being addressed. Cliff's syntax was very delayed in structural development, with verbal responses characterized by short, grammatically immature phrases. Verb conjugations were elementary and subject/predicate sentences were minimal (e.g., "tell 'no pussycat, no' "). Most responses assumed an understood subject, such as "Yell," "Kick harder," and "Sit there." Poor retrieval and organization were also evidenced with the increased expressive language demand.

The *Test of Problem Solving* represents a more complex, integrated language processing task. Cliff's performance on this assessment instrument was significantly diminished compared to age equivalency, percentiles, and standard scores for other more focused language tests. The language processing demand to integrate semantic, syntactic, and pragmatic skills appeared extremely problematic for Cliff.

Informal Evaluation Observations

Cliff's receptive comprehension of language was functionally appropriate. He followed directions presented by the examiner and complied, although repeated comments to maintain attention and motivation were necessary throughout the testing session. Cliff's expressive language was immature in syntactic construction, demonstrating form and content deficits. His word retrieval inaccuracies were very apparent during increased language demand situations. Cliff verbally responded, but his responses were often slightly inaccurate or he generated generic, nonspecific language. His expressive language was disorganized and impulsive in content.

Behavioral components also appeared to contribute to Cliff's struggle to interpret and respond to auditory language information. His body was constantly in motion, and Cliff seemed to enjoy trying to play the role of clown. Avoidance and whining occurred frequently, particularly as tasks increased in cognitive demand. Cliff appeared to be aware of difficulties and, rather than attract negative attention for errors in responses, chose to attract negative attention for acting out.

Conclusions

Cliff's language development was generally commensurate with age expectations in the areas of receptive vocabulary (*PPVT*), auditory memory (*ACLC & ITPA*), single word retrieval (*TWF*), and focused receptive/expressive language (*LPT & ASSET*). Language processing deficits were evidenced by inconsistencies and splintering in language performance (*ASSET & LPT*) and poor expressive problem solving/reasoning (*TOPS*). Language retrieval and organization for larger, more complex expressive ideas were also apparent (*TOPS*).

Language processing is the ability to attach meaning to auditorily received information of increasing cognitive complexity. Language processing presumes adequate development in fundamental receptive and expressive language abilities, i.e., general vocabulary, concepts, articulation, syntax, etc. The deficit is subtle and is usually evidenced as academic demands become more auditory modality based. Early school programming relies on multimodality teaching, i.e., a combination of visual, tactile, and auditory stimuli. A child with language processing deficits is able to compensate for auditory weaknesses with visual and experiential modalities. As the auditory demand increases and academic tasks become more abstract, the student begins experiencing difficulty and frustration. If it goes undetected, it usually results in a learning disability based on language deficits.

The behavioral profile presented by Clifton was consistent with research on students with-language-learning disabilities. In the presence of normal intellectual function, a student develops self-awareness of deficits and attempts to disguise them through purposely distracting authority attention elsewhere. The use of generic, impulsive, immature expressive language is often considered intentional rather than as a primary symptom of a legitimate neurological difference/deficit. Cliff's activity level, history of motoric involvement, and pattern of language inconsistencies is also typical of children with Attention Deficit Hyperactivity Disorder. Focused attention was a struggle, and pharmaceutical intervention should be considered.

Recommendations

Speech-language therapy is recommended in conjunction with classroom consultation and/or learning disabilities resource assistance. The inconsistencies present in Cliff's learning profile should respond well to the introduction of compensatory techniques to offset deficits, and remedial services should not need to be long term in duration. Initiation of trial medication to improve focused attention and modify behavioral aspects should further enhance remediation benefits.

Specific recommendations are the following:

Speech-Language Therapy

1. Language processing inconsistencies in a hierarchy of cognitive demand should be addressed initially to fill in basic language development. The level of associations should be the starting point, with expansion into other focused language tasks of similar cognitive complexity. Examples of language areas include the Boehm concepts, antonyms, synonyms, and homonyms. Suggested therapy materials could include the *Language Processing Kit* and the *Handbook of Exercises for Language Processing (HELP)* series.

2. Problem solving and verbal reasoning should be addressed, beginning with focused one-dimensional problem solving, i.e., one specific task identified, such as determining solutions. Gradually work toward more integrated multidimensional problem solving, and stabilize into everyday situations. Examples of therapy resources include *The TOPS Kit, Elementary* (LinguiSystems, Inc.); and *Think Spots: Drawing Solutions, Using Logic, Finding Facts, Following Directions, Relying on Reason,* etc. (Remedia Publications).

3. Introduce compensatory cuing strategies to facilitate better retrieval and organization of expressive language. An imposed latency might be beneficial to remove impulsive responses and encourage careful processing. The *Language Processing Kit* (LinguiSystems, Inc.) has a chapter and charts to initiate a compensatory program.

4. Syntactic expansion in complexity should be encouraged in conjunction with language processing goals. Higher-level forms and structures will need to be encouraged,

modeled, and required. Possible remediation sources include *No-Glamour Grammar* and *SPARC for Grammar* (LinguiSystems, Inc.).

5. Consultation with classroom teachers is necessary to insure utilization of cues and prompts to facilitate expressive language retrieval and organization. Impulsive answering should be discouraged, and response time pressures should be removed until Cliff's accuracy has improved. Efficiency in response will be secondary to accuracy in the initial stages of intervention.

Classroom and Home Suggestions

1. Encourage Cliff to take his time before responding. Provide cues and prompts, such as the beginning sound, to help focus his retrieval of language. Eventually he will learn to self-cue for language retrieval, and adult intervention can be decreased. Allow additional time to encourage the necessary latency, which facilitates more accurate processing.

2. Request expansion in Cliff's expressive responses to promote better syntactic development and use in daily communication. Don't fill in or complete responses for him. Assist him in formulating a more age-appropriate response, and once the sentence has been generated, go back and ask the original question to give him the opportunity to respond, independently incorporating the language just generated.

3. Don't accept "I don't know," silly responses, or inappropriate behavior from Cliff when he is capable of better. Teach him to request additional time or information (cues) rather than giving up. Impose natural consequences if he does not participate in using cues to retrieve desired information.

4. Provide multimodality presentation whenever possible to assist Cliff's ability to interpret and stay on track when attempting to process auditory information. Use supplemental visual or gestural cues to facilitate his attention and accurate interpretation of stimuli.

5. Short periods of physical activity (walking around the room, down the hall, etc.) during the school day may be necessary to expel Cliff's excess energy and encourage better focus on academic tasks.

I appreciated the opportunity to evaluate Clifton. Please contact me if I can be of further assistance to address questions or concerns.

Sincerely,
Gail J. Richard, Ph.D., CCC-SLP

Conclusion

THE FAR SIDE   By GARY LARSON

"And so you just threw everything together?
... Mathews, a posse is something
you have to *organize*."

We began with a visual processing task to discriminate a cowboy on a horse, so it seems only fitting to close with another cartoon from the old West. You have been on a great adventure as you journeyed through this book. You might have discovered new territory within speech-language pathology and audiology. You have felt the heat of frustration as you struggled to understand new-fangled concepts and models for processing. You could have been overwhelmed by the vast open spaces contained on the continuum of processing.

But the message should be reinforcing now that you've come to the end of the trail. Processing remediation isn't anything new—it's a new perspective in the treatment approach. You have all the ingredients to be effective, just like the sheriff's deputy above. But without imposing a hierarchy of neurological organization on the components, you can't be effective in rounding up and capturing the processing bad guys. Get your posse in order and go get 'em!

180

References

Barrett, M., Huisingh, R., Bowers, L., LoGiudice, C., & Orman, J. 1992. *The Listening Test*. East Moline, IL: LinguiSystems, Inc.

Bloom, B. 1956. *Taxonomy of Educational Objectives: The Classification of Educational Goals, Book 1—Cognitive Domain*. New York, NY: Longman.

Bloom, L. & Lahey, M. 1978. *Language Development and Language Disorders*. New York, NY: John Wiley & Sons.

Bowers, L., Barrett, M., Huisingh, R., Orman, J., & LoGiudice, C. 1994. *The Test of Problem Solving—Revised*. East Moline, IL: LinguiSystems, Inc.

Burns, G. & Watson, B. 1973. Factor analysis of the revised *ITPA* with underachieving children. *Journal of Learning Disabilities*, 6, 371-376.

Cruickshank, W. M. 1966. *The Teacher of Brain-Injured Children*. Syracuse, NY: Syracuse University Press.

DiSimoni, F. 1978. *Token Test for Children*. Austin, TX: Pro-Ed.

Duchan, J. F. & Katz, J. 1983. Language and auditory processing: Top down plus bottom up. In E. Z. Lasky and J. Katz (Eds.) *Central Auditory Disorders: Problems of Speech, Language and Learning*. Baltimore, MD: University Park Press.

Dunn, L. H. & Dunn, L. M. 1997. *The Peabody Picture Vocabulary Test—Third Edition*. Circle Pines, MN: American Guidance Service, Inc.

Fast ForWord User's Guide for Professionals and Educators, Version 1.5. 1999. Berkeley, CA: Scientific Learning Corporation.

Ferre, J. 2000. Complex, not complicated: Understanding children's CAPD. Graduate Forum presentation at Eastern Illinois University, Charleston, IL.

Gaddes, W. H. 1980. *Learning Disabilities and Brain Function—A Neuropsychological Approach*. New York, NY: Springer-Verlag.

Gardner, H. 1993. *Multiple Intelligences: The Theory in Practice*. New York, NY: Basic Books.

Gardner, H. 1983. *Frames of Mind: The Theory of Multiple Intelligences*. New York, NY: Basic Books.

Gerber, A. & Bryen, D. N. 1981. *Language and Learning Disabilities*. Baltimore, MD: University Park Press.

German, D. 1986. *Test of Word Finding*. Allen, TX: DLM Teaching Resources.

Gillet, P. 1993. *Auditory Processes*. Novato, CA: Academic Therapy Publications.

Goldman, R., Fristoe, M., & Woodcock, R. 1974. *Goldman-Fristoe-Woodcock Auditory Series*. Circle Pines, MN: American Guidance Service, Inc.

Hammill, D.D., Mather, N., & Roberts, R. 2001. *Illinois Test of Psycholinguistic Abilities, 3rd Edition*. Austin, TX: Pro-Ed, Inc.

Healy, J. 1990. *Endangered Minds: Why Our Children Can't Think*. New York, NY: Simon & Schuster.

Huisingh, R., Barrett, M., Bowers, L., LoGiudice, C., & Orman, J. 1990. *The WORD Test— Revised*. East Moline, IL: LinguiSystems, Inc.

Jensen, E. 1998. *Teaching with the Brain in Mind*. Association for Supervision and Curriculum Development: Alexandria, VA.

Johnson, D. & Myklebust, H. R. 1967. *Learning Disabilities: Educational Principles and Practices*. New York, NY: Grune & Stratton.

Katz, J. 1978. Evaluation of central dysfunction. In J. Katz (Ed.), *Handbook of Clinical Audiology*, 2nd edition. Baltimore, MD: Williams & Wilkens.

Keith, R. 1986. *SCAN: A Screening Test for Auditory Processing Disorders*. San Antonio, TX: Psychological Corporation.

Keith, R. 1982. *Central Auditory and Language Disorders in Children*. San Diego, CA: College Hill Press.

Kirk, S. A. & Bateman, B. 1962. Diagnosis and remediation of learning disabilities. *Exceptional Children, 29*, 73-78.

Kirk, S. A., McCarthy, J. J., & Kirk, W. D. 1968. *Illinois Test of Psycholinguistic Abilities: Revised Edition.* Urbana, IL: University of Illinois Press.

Lasky E. Z. & Katz, J. (Eds.) 1983. *Central Auditory Processing Disorders—Problems of Speech, Language, and Learning.* Baltimore, MD: University Park Press.

Luria, A. R. 1982. *Language and Cognition.* New York, NY: John Wiley.

Luria, A. R. 1970. The functional organization of the brain. *Scientific American, 222,* 66-78.

Massaro, D. 1975. *Understanding Language: An Information-processing Analysis of Speech Perception, Reading, and Psycholinguistics.* New York, NY: Academic Press.

Myklebust, H. R. 1954. *Auditory Disorders in Children—A Manual for Differential Diagnosis.* New York, NY: Grune & Stratton.

Osgood, C. E. 1957. A behavioral analysis. In *Contemporary Approaches to Cognition.* Cambridge, MA: Harvard University Press.

Pennar, K. 1996. How many smarts do you have? In *Business Week*, September 16, 104-108.

Rees, N. S. 1973. Auditory processing factors in language disorders: The view from Procrustes' bed. *Journal of Speech and Hearing Disorders, 40,* 414-415.

Rees, N. S. 1981. Saying more than we know: Is auditory processing disorder a meaningful concept? In R. Keith (Ed.) *Central Auditory and Language Disorders in Children.* San Diego, CA: College Hill Press.

Richard, G. J. 1987. Assessment alternatives for language processing deficits. Unpublished dissertation. Carbondale, IL: Southern Illinois University.

Richard, G. J. & Hanner, M. A. 1995. *The Language Processing Test—Revised.* East Moline, IL: LinguiSystems, Inc.

Richard, G. J. & Hanner, M. A. 1995. *The Language Processing Kit.* East Moline, IL: LinguiSystems, Inc.

Robertson, C. & Salter, W. 1997. *The Phonological Awareness Test.* East Moline, IL: LinguiSystems, Inc.

Rykman, D. & Wiegerink, R. 1969. The factors of the Illinois Test of Psycholinguistic Abilities: A comparison of 18 factor analyses. *Exceptional Children, 36*, 107-115.

Semel, E., Wiig, E., & Secord, W. 1995. *Clinical Evaluation of Language Fundamentals—Third Edition.* San Antonio, TX: Psychological Corporation.

Simon, C. S. 1991. *Communication Skills and Classroom Success: Assessment and Therapy Methodologies for Language and Learning Disabled Students.* Eau Claire, WI: Thinking Publications.

Sloan, C. 1986. *Treating Auditory Processing Difficulties in Children.* San Diego, CA: Singular Publishing.

Tallal, P. 1976. Rapid auditory processing in normal and disordered language development. *Journal of Speech and Hearing Research, 19*, 561-571.

Tallal, P., Stark, R., Kallman, C., & Mellits, D. 1981. A reexamination of some nonverbal perceptual abilities of language-impaired and normal children as a function of age and sensory modality. *Journal of Speech and Hearing Research, 24*, 351-357.

Tallal, P. & Merzenich, M. 1997. *Fast ForWord* training for children with language-learning problems—National field trial results. Presentation at *ASHA Convention*, Boston, MA.

Vygotsky, L. S. 1962. *Thought and Language.* Cambridge, MA: MIT Press.

Wallach, G. P. & Butler, K. G. 1984. *Language-Learning Disabilities in School Aged Children.* Baltimore, MD: Williams & Wilkins.

Wallach, G. P. & Miller, L. 1988. *Language Intervention and Academic Success.* Boston, MA: College Hill Press.

Weisenberg, L. & Katz, J. 1978. Neurological considerations in audiology. In J. Katz (Ed.) *Handbook of Clinical Audiology*, 2nd ed. Baltimore, MD: Williams & Wilkins.

Wiig, E. & Semel, E. 1980. *Language Assessment and Intervention for the Learning Disabled.* Columbus, OH: Charles Merrill.

Willeford J. A. & Burleigh, J. M. 1985. *Handbook of Central Auditory Processing Disorders in Children.* Orlando, FL: Grune & Stratton, Inc.

Wing, C. S. 1982. Language processes and linguistic levels: A matrix. *Language, Speech, and Hearing Services in Schools, 13*, 2-10.

Answer Key

Chapter 2, page 31
1. B
2. F
3. A
4. D
5. E
6. G
7. C
8. contralateral, ipsilateral
9. left temporal
10. stress, redundancy

Chapter 3, page 43
1. 3
2. 1
3. 1
4. 2
5. 2
6. 3
7. 2
8. 3
9. 1
10. P
11. T
12. S
13. P
14. T
15. T
16. S

19-04-98

185